THE
AMAZING
COLLECTION™

THE
EARLY MINOR
PROPHETS

HOSEA, JOEL, AMOS,

OBADIAH, JONAH, AND MICAH

SET 6

BIG
DREAM
MINISTRIES

© 2005 by Big Dream Ministries, Inc.

No part of *The Amazing Collection*™, whether audio, video, or print, may be reproduced in any form without written permission from Big Dream Ministries, Inc., P.O. Box 324, 12460 Crabapple Road, Suite 202, Alpharetta, Georgia 30004.

ISBN 13: 978-1-932199-06-2
ISBN 10: 1-932199-06-3

Cover design by Brand Navigation and Arvid Wallen
Cover composite image by Getty Images and Corbis
Creative Team: Leigh McLeroy, Kathy Mosier, Pat Reinheimer, Glynese Northam

All Scripture quotations in this publication are taken from the *New American Standard Bible* (NASB), © The Lockman Foundation 1960, 1962, 1963, 1968, 1971, 1972, 1973, 1975, 1977, 1995.

Printed in the United States

9 10 / 17

Welcome to
The Amazing Collection
The Bible, Book by Book

It is amazing how a love letter arriving at just the right time can gladden the heart, refresh the soul, and restore the passion of the beloved. When lovers are separated by distance and can communicate only through the written word, that word becomes the lifeline of their love.

The greatest love letter ever written often sits on our shelves unopened as we go about our lives, sometimes fearful, burdened, anxious, in pain, and in doubt, not knowing that on its pages we can find all we need to live the life we have always wanted.

In this love letter we will discover God, and through Him we will receive hope, assurance, freedom from fear, guidance for everyday life, wisdom, joy, peace, power, and above all, the way to salvation. We will find the life we have always longed for — *abundant* life.

The Bible is simply a love letter compiled into sixty-six books and written over a period of sixteen hundred years by more than forty authors living on three continents. Although the authors came from different backgrounds, there is one message, one theme, one thread that runs throughout the entire Bible from the first book, Genesis, to the last book, Revelation. That message is God's redeeming love for mankind — a message that is as relevant for us today as it was two thousand years ago.

God has written the Bible so that men and women might enter into an intimate relationship with Him and see His character, His works, His power, and His love. It would be tragic to read these books and never come to know your God! Therefore, as you go through this study, listen to the lectures, read the Scripture, and do your daily homework. Make it your heart's desire to know God intimately. Read each page of the Bible as if it were a love letter written by the hand of God to you personally. Bask in His great love, stand in awe of His mighty power, bow before His majesty, and give thanksgiving and adoration to the One who is all-present, all-knowing, all-merciful, and all-loving. He is on every page, and He is speaking to you.

The Bible is a book inspired by God Himself. It is His story, His love letter, His invitation to you to become His child through His Son, Jesus Christ. It is the Word of God . . . indeed, the most Amazing Collection.

CONTENTS

MAPS, CHARTS, AND DIAGRAMS

WORKBOOK GUIDE

The Amazing Collection is a study of the Bible, book by book. In this sixth study, we'll look at the first six of the twelve minor prophets in the Bible. The following will acquaint you with the design of this series.

The entire Bible will be studied one book at a time through a teaching video and a written study. The teaching video includes music to stir the heart, graphics to enlighten the mind, and a personal testimony to bring the theme of that particular book to life.

The workbook contains:

1. An introduction to summarize each book.

2. Outlines to be used while watching each of the teaching videos. The answers to the outline blanks are given during the videos and can also be found in the key at the back of your workbook.

3. *Learning for Life* discussion questions to be used after viewing the videos. (If your group is large, we recommend forming small discussion groups.)

4. Five daily lessons of homework for each book.

5. A memory verse for each book.

6. Various maps, charts, and diagrams.

7. A review at the end of each book to refresh your memory. The answers to the review are found in the *Review It!* sections in the margins at the end of the lessons for Day One through Day Four. The fifth review question is a review of the memory verse.

Before you begin the homework, ask God to show you how to apply the truths of Scripture to your own life. At the beginning of each day's lesson in the workbook, there are two choices for the daily reading. The *Complete Read* enables you to read the entire book over the course of that study. During busy times, the *Quick Read* allows you to read a few key chapters or verses from that book. The daily lesson will require a small amount of time each day to complete. Of course, feel free to extend that time with additional study.

One of the incredible things about the Word of God is that you can read the same Scripture at different times in your life and gain new insights with each reading. God's Word is inexhaustible, and it is living; it has the power to produce life-changing results. Our prayer for you as you journey through *The Amazing Collection* is that you will learn for life the purpose, main characters, geography, and time period of every book in the Bible. But above all, we pray that you will come to know more intimately the God of the Bible, His Son Jesus Christ, and the Holy Spirit..

THE EARLY MINOR PROPHETS AT A GLANCE

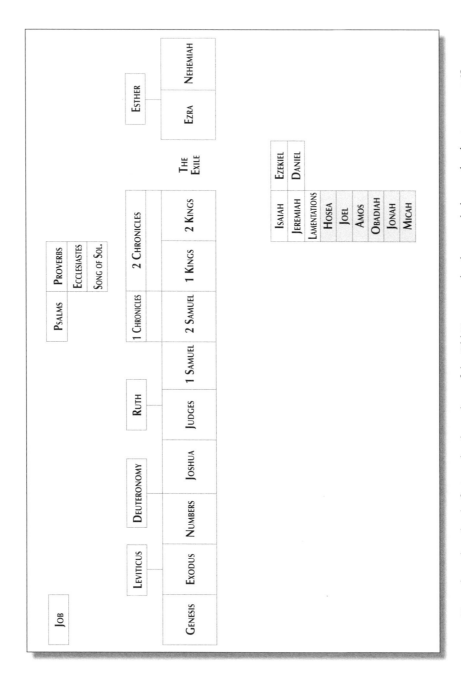

To see how these books fit into the chronology of the Old Testament books as a whole, see the chart on page 168.

	ISRAEL	JUDAH	EXILE IN BABYLONIA	POST-EXILE JERUSALEM	ASSYRIA	EDOM
800 BC		JOEL 835 BC				OBADIAH 848 BC
700 BC	AMOS 760 BC HOSEA 755 BC	ISAIAH 740 BC MICAH 735 BC			JONAH 793 BC	
722 BC	ISRAEL IS CONQUERED BY ASSYRIA					
600 BC		JEREMIAH 627 BC ZEPHANIAH 632 BC HABAKKUK 607 BC	EZEKIEL 592 BC DANIEL 605 BC		NAHUM 664 BC	
586 BC	JUDAH IS EXILED TO BABYLON					
500 BC		LAMENTATIONS 586 BC		HAGGAI 520 BC ZECHARIAH 520 BC		
400 BC				MALACHI 432 BC		
400 BC 0 BC	400 SILENT YEARS					

JESUS CHRIST THE MESSIAH IS BORN

OVERVIEW OF THE EARLY MINOR PROPHETS

The following pages provide an overview of each of the books you will be studying in this set. They are designed to be cut out and used as quick reference cards with the main facts of the book on the front and the memory verse on the back.

You might find it helpful to laminate them and carry them with you on a ring or keep them in a card holder in a place where you'll be able to refer to them often.

It is our hope that this will be a tool that will help you truly learn these books for life.

HOSEA
Israel's Spiritual Adultery

WHO:

Hosea

Gomer

WHAT:

Hosea's Tragic
Marriage Illustrated
Israel's Spiritual
Adultery

WHERE:

Israel

Time Period: 755–715 BC

JOEL
Judah's Locust Invasion

WHO:

Joel

The People of Judah

WHAT:

God's Warning of
Future Judgment
Using a Present-Day
Catastrophe

WHERE:

Judah

Time Period: 835 BC

AMOS
Israel's Plumb Line

WHO:

Amos, a Farmer
Turned Prophet

WHAT:

Israel Was Morally,
Socially, and
Religiously
"Out of Line"

WHERE:

Israel

Time Period: 760 BC

HOSEA
Israel's Spiritual Adultery

"For I delight in loyalty rather than sacrifice,
And in the knowledge of God rather than burnt offerings."

HOSEA 6:6

JOEL
Judah's Locust Invasion

"Yet even now," declares the LORD,
"Return to Me with all your heart,
And with fasting, weeping and mourning;
And rend your heart and not your garments."

JOEL 2:12-13

AMOS
Israel's Plumb Line

"Take away from Me the noise of your songs;
I will not even listen to the sound of your harps.
"But let justice roll down like waters
And righteousness like an ever-flowing stream."

AMOS 5:23-24

OBADIAH
Edom's Doom Announced

WHO:
Obadiah

WHAT:
Prophecy of
Edom's Destruction

WHERE:
Edom

Time Period: Unknown (Thought to Be 848–841 BC)

JONAH
Nineveh's Destruction Delayed

WHO:
Jonah

A Large Fish

Some Sailors

The Ninevites

WHAT:
Rebellious Prophet
Repents and Leads
Nineveh's Revival

WHERE:
Israel

The Sea

Nineveh, Capital
of Assyria

Time Period: 793–753 BC

MICAH
Judah and Israel's Indictment

WHO:
Micah

The People of Israel
and Judah

WHAT:
God's Verdict,
Judgment, and
Promise of the
Messiah

WHERE:
Jerusalem

Samaria

Time Period: 735–700 BC

OBADIAH
Edom's Doom Announced

"As you have done, it will be done to you.
Your dealings will return on your own head."

OBADIAH 15

JONAH
Nineveh's Destruction Delayed

You are a gracious and compassionate God, slow to anger
and abundant in lovingkindness, and one who
relents concerning calamity.

JONAH 4:2

MICAH
Judah and Israel's Indictment

And what does the LORD require of you
But to do justice, to love kindness,
And to walk humbly with your God?

MICAH 6:8

INTRODUCTION TO
THE EARLY MINOR PROPHETS

For the purpose of this study we will divide the Minor Prophets into two sets: The Early Minor Prophets and The Later Minor Prophets. This will make our study of these prophets more manageable. You'll see some of this information repeated in the introduction to the next set, The Later Minor Prophets.

It is unfortunate that the word *minor* has been attached to these last twelve books of the Old Testament. As we explained in the introduction to The Major Prophets, the Minor Prophets are shorter in length, to be sure, but no less significant than the Major Prophets in regard to prominence of authorship or importance of material.

The scope of these books is broad indeed. Chronologically, they span more than four centuries from approximately 848 to 425 BC. Geographically, they touch Israel, Judah, Syria, Moab, Ammon, Edom, Egypt, Ethiopia, and Assyria. Thematically, they explore such topics as love, mercy, compassion, wrath, judgment, holiness, obedience, disobedience, hope, repentance, and many more.

As you begin your study of these books, be prepared for gripping and graphic portrayals of both God and man: Hosea's picture of God's love for his adulterous people symbolized by the prophet's love for his adulterous wife; Jonah's portrayal of himself as a disobedient, runaway prophet pursued by a patient God; Amos's colorful visions of God's judgment that would come because of his continued disobedience; and Obadiah's classic portrait of pride.

The setting of these books may be ancient, but their message is modern. You will meet the eternal God in them — and you will meet yourself. Welcome to the Minor Prophets whose message is major.

HOSEA

ONE

[Israel's Spiritual Adultery]

"For I delight in loyalty rather than sacrifice,

And in the knowledge of God rather than

burnt offerings."

HOSEA 6:6

HOSEA
[Israel's Spiritual Adultery]

INTRODUCTION

We'll begin our study of the Minor Prophets with the book of Hosea. Hosea is one of only two writing prophets (the other one being Amos) who ministered to the northern kingdom of Israel. Together they delivered a solid message of hard-hitting truth. Hosea spoke clearly of the people's sin and coming judgment but always couched his message in God's incredibly patient love. Amos spoke clearly of the people's sin and coming judgment without reminding the people of God's love.

As you read and study Hosea, you will feel the tension of love and judgment again and again. God was doing all he could to break through the shell of His people's insistent rebellion but to no avail.

There may be no greater illustration of a prophet's own experience mirroring God's experience than in the book of Hosea. Your Day Three study will introduce you to a personal trauma in the life of Hosea that reflected what God Himself was experiencing. Be sure to take enough time to really sense the emotion and drama of the prophet's ordeal.

Welcome to The Early Minor Prophets and specifically to the book of Hosea. Look for God to touch your heart with its challenging message.

HOSEA
[Israel's Spiritual Adultery]

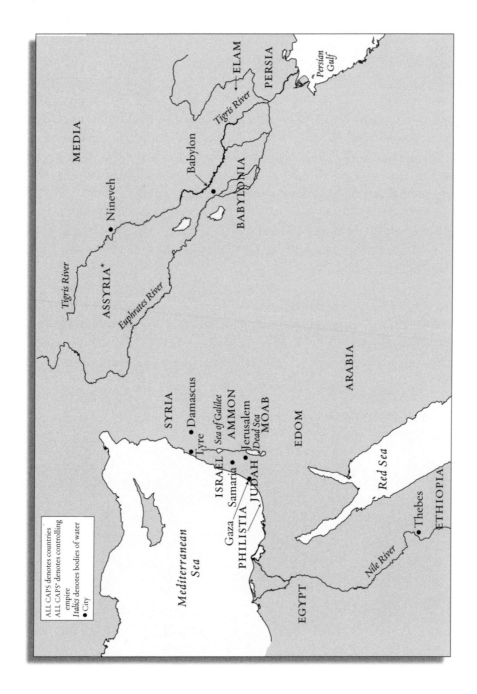

H OSEA
[Israel's Spiritual Adultery]

OVERVIEW

WHO: Author: Hosea
Main Characters: Hosea, Gomer

WHAT: A warning of impending judgment to the northern kingdom of Israel

WHEN: Hosea ministered between 755 and 715 BC

WHERE: The northern kingdom of Israel

WHY: God's love, faithfulness, and justice are illustrated through Hosea's marriage to his adulterous wife, Gomer

I. THE BACKGROUND OF HOSEA

    A. The marriage: God entered into a _____ relationship with Israel at Mount Sinai.

        1. God had given the people _____ through the law, His promises, and His presence.

        2. God had given the people His _____ through His provision and His protection.

    B. The adultery: The people wanted to enjoy their _____ and so went "a-whoring."

II. THE MANIFESTATION OF SPIRITUAL ADULTERY DURING THE FINAL YEARS OF ISRAEL

    A. Jeroboam II (793–753 BC) brought _____ to Israel.

    B. Zechariah (753 BC) reigned six months and was _____ by Shallum.

    C. Shallum (752 BC) reigned one month and was _____ by Menahem.

    D. Menahem (752–742 BC) reigned ten years.

1. He ripped open the _____ women of Tipsah.

2. He died of natural causes.

E. Pekahiah (742–740 BC) reigned two years and was _____
by Pekah.

F. Pekah (752–732 BC) reigned twenty years and was _____
by Hoshea.

G. Hoshea (732–723 BC) reigned _____ years.

1. Assyria _____ Samaria, the capital of Israel, for the last
three years of Hoshea's reign.

2. Israel was _____ by Assyria (722 BC).

3. Assyria _____ the Israelites who survived.

III. THE MARRIAGE OF HOSEA

A. God commanded Hosea to take a wife who was a _____ .

B. Three children came from the marriage:

1. Jezreel: God will bring _____ in the valley of Jezreel,
which means "God sows."

2. Lo-ruhamah: "She is not loved" because God would no longer show
_____ on Israel.

3. Lo-ammi: "Not my _____ " as the Lord would no
longer regard Israel as His people.

C. Gomer became a _____ .

D. She ended up in _____ .

E. Hosea _____ his wife and bought her back from slavery.

IV. THE MESSAGE OF HOSEA

A. God deeply _____ His people.

B. The people had sinned against God.

1. They were _____ .

2. They were _____ .

3. They were _____ .

4. Their _____ enjoyed the sins of the people.

5. They were _____ .

6. They made foreign _____ .

7. They were _____ .

C. God would bring about judgment.

   1. He would raise up _____ .

   2. Israel would be _____ .

   3. Survivors would be _____ .

   4. They would no longer have God's _____ .

   5. They would not enjoy the _____ God had given them.

D. God will _____ His people in the future.

   1. They will once again _____ the land.

   2. He will be their _____/God.

   3. He will shower them with _____ .

   4. There will never again be a _____ .

APPLICATION

In Hosea, God compares His love for us to that of a husband for his bride. Are you a faithful bride to God, or are you an adulteress?

H OSEA
[Israel's Spiritual Adultery]

LEARNING FOR LIFE

1. Who was Hosea's audience, and why was God about to bring judgment upon them?

2. How does earthly adultery compare to spiritual adultery?

3. What emotions would one experience if her marriage partner were unfaithful?

4. What lessons did you learn about the heart of God in the book of Hosea?

5. How does Hosea's response to Gomer compare to God's response to His wayward children?

6. Hosea bought his wife, Gomer, back from slavery. Who rescued us from the slavery of sin? (See Romans 6:6-11.)

HOSEA
[Israel's Spiritual Adultery]

DAY ONE

COMPLETE READ: Chapters 1–3
QUICK READ: Chapter 2

THE BIG PICTURE

> After Jeroboam, what we see in the prophecy of Hosea is the last few swirls as the kingdom of Israel goes down the drain.
> — DAVID ALLAN HUBBARD

Sin had riddled the nation of Israel, and idolatry was running rampant. Into this scene of spiritual desperation God sent the prophet Hosea, a family man. But Hosea had problems of his own. His wife was an adulteress who left him for other lovers. Hosea refused to accept that behavior and bought her back from the depths to which her lust had taken her — the slave market. Thus the loyal love of a husband for a wandering wife became a living illustration of God's overtures to His betrothed and unfaithful lover, Israel. Hosea's wife had run after other lovers, but Hosea took her back. God's beloved nation had also run after other lovers (gods), and He too was willing to welcome her back.

Our Heavenly Lover used the lips of Hosea to recount Israel's sin over and over again and at the same time to restate His loyal love for them. His love must discipline, but it will also restore. The name Hosea means "salvation." And in this message to his sinful countrymen in the northern kingdom of Israel, Hosea offered salvation from God if only they would turn from their idolatry and place their trust in Him.

The dearest idol I have known,
Whate'er that idol be;
Help me to tear it from thy throne,
And worship only thee.
—WILLIAM COWPER, eighteenth-century hymn writer, from his hymn *Walking with God*

Hosea 1:1 says that Hosea ministered during the reigns of four kings of Judah and one king of Israel, which would place his forty-year ministry between the years of 755 and 715 BC. The reign of Jeroboam II (793–753 BC) was a period of brilliance in Israel. He was a talented administrator and military strategist who reexpanded the nation's borders back to those of Solomon's time. He erected magnificent buildings and took advantage of four trade routes running through the land, breathing life into the copper, weaving, and dyeing industries.

Everything in Israel looked great on the outside, but on the inside, things were rotten. The people offered sacrifices, held the required feasts, and called on the name of Yahweh, but it meant nothing. It was all a sham.

Once Jeroboam II died, a series of weak and vicious kings ruled. The brilliance of Jeroboam's accomplishments faded. As the people drifted further and further from God, Hosea illustrated and taught about God's love for them, regardless of their sin. This love did not mean that God would ignore their sin but that if they would repent, He would receive them back. Without repentance, God promised sure and swift judgment.

God's message to the people through the prophet Hosea was that there was no knowledge of God in the land. Therefore, He would discipline them through the cruelty of and captivity by Assyria.

The chart that follows shows the two major divisions of the book.

Our attitude toward sin is more self-centered than God-centered. We are more concerned about our own "victory" over sin than we are about the fact that our sin grieves the heart of God.

—JERRY BRIDGES, author and Bible teacher

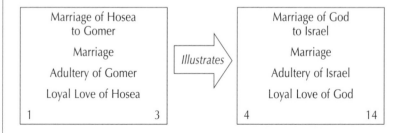

Marriage of Hosea to Gomer		Marriage of God to Israel
Marriage	*Illustrates*	Marriage
Adultery of Gomer		Adultery of Israel
Loyal Love of Hosea		Loyal Love of God
1 3		4 14

As you read Hosea, look for three or four verses you feel could be valuable to your understanding of God and your walk with Him. Jot them down on 3 x 5 cards and carry them with you throughout the week. Refer to them regularly, and at the end of the week decide if you should commit one or more of them to memory.

What are your thoughts on chapter 2, your Quick Read for the day? Jot down your feelings, impressions, and questions. As you go through the week, watch to see if your impressions are confirmed or your questions answered.

However many and however great and burdensome your sins may be, with God there is greater mercy.

—TIKHON OF ZADONSK, eighteenth-century Russian monk and bishop

MEMORY VERSE

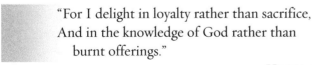

"For I delight in loyalty rather than sacrifice,
And in the knowledge of God rather than
   burnt offerings."

HOSEA 6:6

REVIEW IT!
The theme of Hosea is that God desires knowledge of Himself above all else.

H OSEA
[Israel's Spiritual Adultery]

IMPORTANT
Hosea contains twenty-four references to Baal worship and its accompanying rituals.

DAY TWO

COMPLETE READ: Chapters 4–6
QUICK READ: Chapter 4

A CRUCIAL CHAPTER

In his book *The Pursuit of God,* A. W. Tozer concludes one of the chapters with this prayer:

> Father, I want to know Thee, but my coward heart fears to give up its toys. I cannot part with them without inward bleeding, and I do not try to hide from Thee the terror of the parting. I come trembling, but I do come. Please root from my heart all those things which I have cherished so long and which have become a very part of my living self, so that Thou mayest enter and dwell there without a rival. Then shalt Thou make the place of Thy feet glorious. Then shall my heart have no need of the sun to shine in it, for Thyself wilt be the light of it, and there shall be no night there. In Jesus' Name, Amen.[1]

I clearly recognize that all good is in God alone, and that in me, without Divine grace, there is nothing but deficiency.

—CATHERINE OF GENOA, fifteenth-century Italian mystic and saint

Chapter 4 is a Crucial Chapter because it pictures clearly the complaint God had against the Israelites that eventually brought judgment. As you read this chapter, your Quick Read for today, respond to the following questions.

Assume that an Israelite hearing this message was convinced of his wrongdoing and desired to respond to Hosea's message. Assume also that he wanted to respond in this way: "Please root from my heart all those things which I have cherished so long and which have become a very part of my living self." On the basis of the passage, what things would he or she want rooted out?

Also based on the Tozer passage, what would it take for God to "enter and dwell there without a rival"?

Now, instead of reading the story of Israel's life, read the story of your life. Assume that you also want to respond to Tozer's words, "Please root from my heart all those things which I have cherished so long and which have become a very part of my living self." What things do you want rooted out?

I shall never do otherwise if You leave me to myself; it is You who must hinder my falling and mend what is amiss.

—Brother Lawrence, seventeenth-century French Carmelite monk and "kitchen saint"

What would it look like in your life if Tozer's phrase "so that Thou mayest enter and dwell there without a rival" were actually accomplished?

Tell God what is on your heart right now.

REVIEW IT!
Chapter 4 is a Crucial
Chapter because it
pictures clearly God's
complaint against the
Israelites.

MEMORY VERSE

"For I delight in loyalty rather than sacrifice,
And in the knowledge of God rather than
burnt offerings."

HOSEA 6:6

H OSEA
[Israel's Spiritual Adultery]

DAY THREE

COMPLETE READ: Chapters 7–9
QUICK READ: Chapters 1 and 3

A PROMINENT PLAYER

David Allan Hubbard, in his book *With Bands of Love*, writes of Hosea,

> As few men before or after, he had passed through refining fires of personal suffering and emerged free from the dross of bitterness and resentment which have clouded many a lesser soul. His compassion for his people and his understanding of God's heartbreak and disappointment are apparent on almost every page.[2]

The ministry to which God called Hosea is unenviable to say the least. He either married Gomer when she was already a harlot, or she became one after he married her (Hosea 1:2). Either way, once she left him to chase after other men, she ended up in the slave market, having been rejected by her lovers (3:1-3).

Prior to running off with other men, Gomer had borne Hosea two sons and a daughter who were given names that foretold the coming judgment of God on His people. Read 1:3-9 and in your own words give the meaning of the children's names.

DID YOU KNOW?
One writer has subtitled the book of Hosea "The Prodigal Wife."

There is no agony like bearing an untold story inside of you.
—MAYA ANGELOU, poet and writer

NOTE
The book of Hosea is referred to directly or indirectly thirty times in the New Testament.

Names were much more important and descriptive of a person in biblical days than they are in our contemporary culture. Realizing that everyone around him would understand the meaning of these names, what kinds of emotional issues do you think Hosea might have had to face?

Hosea 3:1-3 records Hosea redeeming his wife from the slave market. The price of a common slave at that time was thirty pieces of silver, but he was able to redeem her for only fifteen. She had lowered herself to such a place that she was worth only half the price of a common slave. The mention of barley speaks of her utter worthlessness, as this was the food of animals.

Write in your own words what Hosea said to Gomer in verse 3.

Paul spoke openly about his pain, not in complaint, but as a reminder that the abundant life of following Jesus means abundant opportunities to draw near to Him in hard times, not an abundance of pleasant circumstances and good feelings.

—LARRY CRABB,
The Pressure's Off

Describe the struggle you imagine he had with his heart and mind as he redeemed her.

Evidently Hosea lived with this personal struggle for a number of years as it emerged and was then resolved. Only then did God free him to speak to the people about their spiritual adultery as it related to God.

Consider the heart shaping God must have accomplished in Hosea during these difficult years and explain the impact this shaping would have had on his prophetic ministry.

Hosea 11:1-4 relates God's love for Israel and their spurning of His love. If you had heard Hosea preach this message and known his personal struggles, how might you have responded?

What life messages has God taught you through trials and suffering that you have the opportunity to share from time to time?

MEMORY VERSE

"For I delight in loyalty rather than sacrifice, And in the knowledge of God rather than burnt offerings."

HOSEA 6:6

REVIEW IT!
Hosea is a Prominent Player because his personal life embodied his message.

H OSEA
[Israel's Spiritual Adultery]

AMAZING!
Hosea contains at least forty-five vivid word pictures.

DAY FOUR

COMPLETE READ: Chapters 10–11
QUICK READ: Chapter 7

A NOTABLE FEATURE

When Leonardo da Vinci was painting his masterpiece *The Last Supper*, he chose a young man, a chorister with the Milan Cathedral, to sit for the character of Christ. It took years for the painting to be completed, and when da Vinci lacked only one more character to paint — Judas Iscariot — he took to the streets of Rome to find his model. He came upon a man, shoulders bent, with a look of cold, hardened evil — exactly how he had imagined Judas to be. Later, in the studio, the man from the streets began to look around as if he knew the place. He turned to da Vinci and said sadly, "Maestro, I was in this studio twenty-five years ago. I, then, sat for Christ."[3]

I think that man is lost indeed who has lost the sense of shame.

—PLAUTUS, Roman comic dramatist

Like this man, Israel had spiraled from glory to shame. Read Hosea 9:10 and see again their former glory:

> I found Israel like grapes in the wilderness;
> I saw your forefathers as the earliest fruit on the
> > fig tree in its first season.
> But they came to Baal-peor and devoted
> > themselves to shame,
> And they became as detestable as that which they
> > loved.

God had high hopes for Israel as a nation. He saw them as "grapes in the wilderness" — fruit in an unexpected place — and as "the earliest fruit on the fig tree in its first season" — a cause for celebration! But sin had abounded over the years and taken its toll; the nation of glory had become a nation of shame.

In the space of fourteen chapters, the book of Hosea contains 146 statements chronicling the sins of Israel. Chapter 7, your Quick Read, contains at least twenty of those statements. Jot down as many as you see.

DON'T MISS IT!
The terms *harlot* and *harlotry* occur twenty-one times in the book of Hosea.

Hosea didn't confine himself to technical descriptions of Israel's sin. In an attempt to break through to their hard hearts, he used descriptive analogies to show what their sin was like. Read the following verses and record the phrases he used to describe Israel's sin. In your own words write down what you think he meant.

4:16

7:11

8:9

13:3

Every method put to use to mortify sin which is not by the Holy Spirit is doomed to failure. Every system which attempts to deal with sin without Christ and the Holy Spirit is legalistic and miserable.

—JOHN OWEN, seventeenth-century Puritan theologian

Hosea went even further, painting a vivid picture of how God would respond to their sin. Again, record his descriptions in the following verses and explain what you think he meant. 5:12

13:7-8

Based on today's study, briefly state God's feelings about sin.

But as always, God doesn't end there. Following His discipline, God offered hope and restoration for rebellious Israel. Read 14:4-8 and put into words the change of tone and feeling you sense.

Are there areas in your life that have spiraled from glory to shame? Can you repent of them and then bask in the healing truths you just read?

MEMORY VERSE

"For I delight in loyalty rather than sacrifice,
And in the knowledge of God rather than
burnt offerings."

HOSEA 6:6

REVIEW IT!
A Notable Feature of Hosea is the many ways in which sin is described and pictured.

HOSEA
[Israel's Spiritual Adultery]

God's Character

DAY FIVE

DID YOU NOTICE?
Hosea calls Israel
"Ephraim" thirty-seven
times in the book.

COMPLETE READ: Chapters 12–14
QUICK READ: Chapter 6

A TIMELESS PRINCIPLE

J. I. Packer writes in *Knowing God*,

> Knowing about God is crucially important for the living of our lives. As it would be cruel to an Amazonian tribesman to fly him to London, put him down without explanation in Trafalgar Square and leave him, as one who knew nothing of English or England, to fend for himself, so we are cruel to ourselves if we try to live in this world without knowing about the God whose world it is and who runs it. The world becomes a strange, mad, painful place, and life in it a disappointing and unpleasant business, for those who do not know about God. Disregard the study of God, and you sentence yourself to stumble and blunder through life blindfolded, as it were, with no sense of direction and no understanding of what surrounds you. This way you can waste your life and lose your soul."[4]

God is continually drawing us to Himself in everything we experience.
—GERARD HUGHES, author of *God of Surprises*

This knowing about God is a unique kind of knowledge, which the following contrasts make clear.

NOT	BUT
Knowledge *about* God	Knowledge *of* God
To *see* the *fact* of	To *feel* the *force* of
Knowledge as *acquisition*	Knowledge as *impression*
Mastering the knowledge	*Being mastered* by the knowledge
Knowing *propositions*	Knowing the *Person*

NOTE
About the time Hosea
began to minister,
the city of Rome was
founded (735 BC).

In short, you can know all about God and yet not know God. The burden Hosea tried to convey is our theme: that God desires this true knowledge of Himself above all else. Time after time Hosea introduced this theme. Read the following verses and briefly explain what each contributes to this concept of knowing God.

2:20

4:1

4:6

5:4

6:3

6:6

8:2

13:4

Once you become aware that the main business that you are here for is to know God, most of life's problems fall into place of their own accord.

—J. I. PACKER,
theologian, professor, and author of *Knowing God*

In light of these truths, what seems to stand in opposition to knowing God? (It might help to check the immediate context of the verses.)

If you were to choose one of these verses to meditate on for the next month, which one would it be and why?

How are you doing at knowing God?

The New Testament addresses this truth often. When you have time, consider John 17:3; Philippians 3:8-11; 2 Peter 1:2-3; 1 John 2:3-6; 4:7-8.

As you finish this week of study, take time to pray as Paul did for the Ephesians:

> For this reason I too, having heard of the faith in the Lord Jesus which exists among you and your love for all the saints, do not cease giving thanks for you, while making mention of you in my prayers; that the God of our Lord Jesus Christ, the Father of glory, may give to you a spirit of wisdom and of revelation in the *knowledge of Him*. I pray that the eyes of your heart may be enlightened, so that you will know what is the hope of His calling, what are the riches of the glory of His inheritance in the saints, and what is the surpassing greatness of His power toward us who believe. (Ephesians 1:15-19, emphasis added)

Jesus came to earth to tell us He is the way, the truth, and the life. His death opened the way into God's presence, the greatest blessing of all. His teaching made clear the truth that life does not consist in a return to Eden's comforts; it doesn't even consist in graduation to heaven's bliss. True life is knowing God.
—LARRY CRABB, *The Pressure's Off*

MEMORY VERSE

"For I delight in loyalty rather than sacrifice,
And in the knowledge of God rather than
    burnt offerings."

HOSEA 6:6

HOSEA
[Israel's Spiritual Adultery]

REVIEW

1. The theme of Hosea is that God desires _____ of Himself above all else.

2. Chapter 4 is a Crucial Chapter because it pictures clearly God's _____ against the Israelites.

3. _____ is a Prominent Player because his personal life embodied his message.

4. A Notable Feature of Hosea is the many ways in which _____ is described and pictured.

5. "'For I delight in _____ rather than sacrifice,
And in the knowledge of God rather than burnt offerings.'"

HOSEA 6:_____

JOEL

TWO

"Yet even now," declares the LORD,

"Return to Me with all your heart,

And with fasting, weeping and mourning;

And rend your heart and not your garments."

JOEL 2:12-13

JOEL
[Judah's Locust Invasion]

INTRODUCTION

You have just finished studying Hosea, one of two prophets sent by God to the northern kingdom of Israel. This week you will encounter the earliest of God's prophets commissioned to preach to the people of the southern kingdom of Judah—the prophet Joel.

Joel is a short book, but it packs a spiritual and chronological wallop. Spiritually, Joel held nothing back as he challenged God's people about their sinful lives and implored them to repent and change their ways. Chronologically, Joel not only dealt with a recent disaster of nature (you will study this in Day Two), but he also forecast centuries ahead to speak of events that will take place near the end of time. The prophet masterfully related the recent natural disaster to the end-of-time events. This comparison is both graphic and powerful.

You will see much of the greatness and power of God tightly packed into this short and tense book. And hopefully your understanding of and respect for this greatness and power will deepen.

J OEL
[Judah's Locust Invasion]

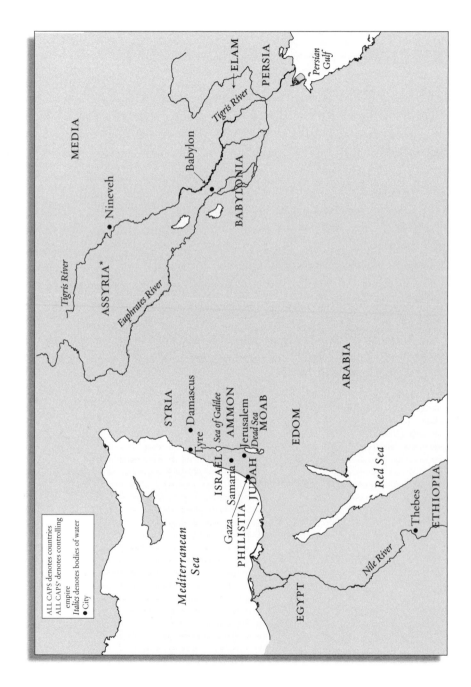

JOEL
[Judah's Locust Invasion]

OVERVIEW

WHO: Author: Joel
Main Characters: The people of Judah

WHAT: A warning about God's judgment (the Day of the Lord) that uses a present-day catastrophe to describe future tribulations

WHEN: The date is debated, but Joel is thought to have prophesied around 835 BC; contemporaries: Elijah, Elisha

WHERE: The southern kingdom of Judah

WHY: To give the nation of Judah warning of God's impending judgment, as well as hope for the future

I. HISTORIC INVASION: THE DAY OF THE LOCUSTS (JOEL 1)

A. Judah's situation: The people were dealing with devastation from a plague of

_____ .

B. Joel's solution: Judah was to see the plague as a _____ and

_____ .

II. FUTURE INVASIONS: THE DAY OF THE LORD (JOEL 2–3)

A. The invasion would be like an enormous, powerful _____ .

B. The call to _____ (to turn back to God) was repeated.

C. Joel announced that God will _____ when the people

_____ .

D. _____ will be poured out on all mankind.

E. Joel looked far into the future and described _____ and its effect upon Israel and her enemies.

  1. _____ who call upon the name of the Lord will be saved.

  2. He encouraged Israel with a vision about _____ .

3. God will have a _____ delivered, and they will be saved.

4. Jerusalem will once again be the _____ city it was meant to be.

5. God will deal with Israel's enemies who will be gathered to the Valley of Jehoshaphat for the battle of _____ .

APPLICATION

One day life as we know it will end as God ushers in a new age. We are to rejoice and live expectantly with that knowledge ever before us.

JOEL
[Judah's Locust Invasion]

LEARNING FOR LIFE

1. Tell something about the theme or message of each prophetical book beginning with Isaiah.

2. Joel introduced a new phrase that had significance not only for Judah but also for the entire world. What is the phrase, what does it mean, and how might it be significant in our future?

3. Joel used a current devastating event in the lives of those living in Judah to warn the people about a coming invasion that would be much worse. What events do you see happening today that could be considered a warning from God about future judgment?

4. Share a time when you ignored an obvious warning and then suffered for it.

5. Discuss ways we can pay attention to God's warnings today and how we might benefit if we do.

JOEL
[Judah's Locust Invasion]

DAY ONE

COMPLETE READ: Chapters 1–3
QUICK READ: Chapter 1

THE BIG PICTURE

Illustrations are like windows: They invite light into an otherwise dark place. The prophet Joel chose an illustration from nature to shine the light of understanding into the hearts of his listeners. Impending judgment from God because of the people's undeterred sin was Joel's subject. To drive home the potential devastation of this judgment, Joel described a locust plague that had recently invaded the nation of Judah. With insatiable appetites, the locusts had consumed everything in their path. Vines, fields, and trees had been left stripped and barren.

And then Joel made his point: This destruction is nothing compared to the devastation that will occur when the Day of the Lord arrives. At that time, God will send a northern army against His people, and the army's overwhelming victory will be a foregone conclusion.

But God offers hope. If His people repent, He will respond by restoring them to their land, pouring out His Spirit upon them, and judging their enemies.

We have a strange illusion that mere time cancels sin.

—C. S. LEWIS, English essayist, novelist, and Christian apologist

The name Joel means "Yahweh is God," an appropriate description of a man who wrote about the power and control of God over both nature and nations. We know nothing of Joel's family except that his father's name was Pethuel (Joel 1:1). We surmise he lived in Jerusalem because of the many statements in the book about Jerusalem and its worship, but we cannot be certain.

Joel prophesied to the southern kingdom of Judah. Although we cannot be sure, we believe that he ministered around 835 BC, making him the second earliest of the writing prophets. To help you place Joel in the chronology of the Old Testament story, know that he prophesied:

DID YOU KNOW?
The prophets Joel and Obadiah were separated by only a decade.

- One hundred years after the nation divided into Israel and Judah in 931 BC

- About the same time as Elisha, who succeeded Elijah

- About one hundred years before Isaiah

- Over two hundred years before Jeremiah

Though Joel's ministry occurred relatively early in the history of the southern kingdom of Judah, Joel sensed a need to warn the people of their rebellion against God, of their need for repentance, and of God's promised forgiveness. He did so by introducing the Day of the Lord, a biblical concept that comes up over and over, especially in the prophetical books but also in the New Testament (see 2 Thessalonians 2:2; 2 Peter 3:10).

Because of the difficulties of interpretation, this is not the place to do a thorough biblical study of the Day of the Lord. But we can say that the Day of the Lord is that period in the end times when judgment will be placed on people and nations for their sin against God and blessing and restoration given for those who trust in Him. When the Day of the Lord begins, we will know that the end of time is near (see 2 Peter 3:10).

It may be a secret sin on earth, but it is open scandal in heaven.
—LEWIS SPERRY CHAFER, American Bible teacher, evangelist, educator, and writer

The Day of the Lord is the unifying theme of Joel as seen in the following chart.

The Day of the Lord in Preview	The Day of the Lord in Progress	
Locust Plague Economic Disaster	God's Dealings with Israel	God's Dealings with the Nations
HISTORY 1	PROPHECY 2	PROPHECY 3

The word *day* occurs nine times in these three chapters, sometimes in the phrase "the day of the Lord" and other times simply as "the day" or "a day." Locate these nine references and write down what each of them adds to the concept of the Day of the Lord. Remember, the Day of the Lord is that future time period of both judgment and blessing.

When you grapple with concepts that show God's control and power, as these three chapters do, how are you impacted personally?

REVIEW IT!
The theme of Joel is the Day of the Lord is coming!

MEMORY VERSE

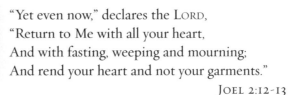

"Yet even now," declares the LORD,
"Return to Me with all your heart,
And with fasting, weeping and mourning;
And rend your heart and not your garments."

JOEL 2:12-13

J OEL
[Judah's Locust Invasion]

DAY TWO

COMPLETE READ: Chapters 1–3
QUICK READ: Chapter 1

UNBELIEVABLE!
A swarm of locusts can completely denude a full-grown fig tree in fifteen minutes!

A NOTABLE FEATURE

Because some prophetical books are so brief, we will occasionally change the daily format in order to adjust our focus of study. In our study of Joel, we will not have a Crucial Chapter or a Prominent Player. Tomorrow we will look at a Timeless Principle, and on Days Four and Five we will investigate topics related to the prophets.

Daniel Da Cruz writes,

> No one who has ever seen the locust at work accuses the Bible account of hyperbole. In 1926 and 1927, small swarms of the African migratory locusts were spotted in an area 50 by 120 miles on the plains of the river Niger near Timbuktu. The next year swarms invaded Senegal and Sierra Leone. By 1930 the whole of west Africa was flailing away at the pests with everything movable. But the locusts didn't seem to notice; swarms reached Khartoum, more than 2000 miles to the east of Timbuktu, then turned south, spreading across Ethiopia, Kenya, the Belgian Congo, and in 1932, striking into the lush farm land of Angola and Rhodesia. Before the plague finally sputtered out fourteen years after it began, it affected five-million square miles of Africa, an area nearly double the size of the United States.[1]

Beloved men, realize what is true: this world is in haste and the end approaches: and therefore in the world things go from bad to worse.

—GREGORY THE GREAT, sixth-century Italian saint and pope

AMAZING!
One square mile of
a locust swarm can
contain one hundred
million to two hundred
million locusts.

Our Notable Feature is Joel's description of the actual locust plague that had invaded and destroyed the land. Because the people could not forget the devastation of the plague they had endured, they would not miss the impact of Joel's foreshadowing of God's future judgment — especially when he said that it would be even worse.

Read through chapter 1, your Quick Read for today, and write down any examples you find of the severity and destruction of this plague.

What did Joel command the people to do in response to the locust plague? (His injunctions are scattered throughout the chapter.)

God examines both rich and poor, not according to their lands and houses, but according to the riches of their hearts.

—Saint Augustine of Hippo, Carthaginian scholar, philosopher, and church father

Read Joel 1:15. Remember that our study yesterday emphasized the Day of the Lord and the relationship between the historical perspective of chapter 1 and the prophetical orientation of chapters 2 and 3. Write down what you believe to be the purpose and importance of the placement of verse 15 in chapter 1.

As we have said, chapter 1 is a discussion of a historical event used as a tool to encourage the people to think about the future, particularly the end times when everything will change. As you consider our world today, what events or circumstances do you see that could be tools from God to get us to think about the future, particularly the end times? There are no right answers to this question — just record your thoughts.

In light of what you've just written, is there anything in your life that you should evaluate and possibly adjust?

MEMORY VERSE

"Yet even now," declares the LORD,
"Return to Me with all your heart,
And with fasting, weeping and mourning;
And rend your heart and not your garments."

JOEL 2:12-13

JOEL
[Judah's Locust Invasion]

NOTE
Joel 2:28-32 is quoted at length in Acts 2:16-21.

DAY THREE

COMPLETE READ: Chapters 1–3
QUICK READ: Chapter 2:12-20

A TIMELESS PRINCIPLE

Regret over sin is good, but it is not enough.

Remorse over sin is better, but it is still lacking.

Repentance over sin is the goal, but it does not come easily.

Regret is wishing we hadn't done something because we don't like the consequences. Søren Kierkegaard writes, "This kind of repentance [regret] is selfish, a matter of the senses. . . . [It] would drink down all the bitterness of sorrow in a single drought and then hurry on. It wants to get away from guilt."[2]

To do so no more is the truest repentance.
—MARTIN LUTHER, German theologian and religious reformer

Remorse goes deeper and brings agony over doing something wrong in God's eyes. Though not the final step, even this is difficult to attain because as Albert Camus says in his novel *The Fall*, "Each of us insists on being innocent at all cost, even if he has to accuse the whole human race and heaven itself."[3]

Our true destination should be repentance, where we not only regret and truly sorrow over our sin but turn and go in a different direction, away from the sin and toward righteousness.

Joel 2:12-20, your Quick Read for today, describes repentance as Joel desired to see it manifested in the culture of his day. Instead of using the word *repent*, he asked the people to *return* to God, to make movement back to the point of departure. This implies going back to where you were before the sin; returning to a state of cleanness; and dealing with the sin in such a way that it is as if it never occurred because you have owned it, repented of it, and received forgiveness for it.

As you meditate on this short passage, jot down your thoughts on the following questions.

What was Joel asking the people to do?

Describe in your own words the picture of God that radiates from this passage.

Even though verses 18-20 are a potential response of God to people in a different historical and cultural environment than ours, what principles do you see in how God responds to true returning?

Before God can deliver us we must undeceive ourselves.

—Saint Augustine of Hippo, fourth-century bishop in northern Africa

A Puritan prayer in *The Valley of Vision* reminds us of the importance of true repentance:

> Thou dost not play in convincing me of sin,
> Satan did not play in tempting me to it,
> I do not play when I sink in deep mire,
> For sin is no game, no toy, no bauble;
> Let me never forget that the heinousness of sin
> Lies not so much in the nature of the sin
>   committed,
> As in the greatness of the person sinned against.[4]

Describe the impact of these words on your heart.

Is there anything you need to repent of right now? If so, take time to talk with God about it.

After moving from regret to remorse to repentance, it is equally important to revel in the boundless joy of God's grace and forgiveness. As you finish this study today, consider meditating on one Puritan writer's attempt to bask in forgiveness:

> Grant me to hear Thy voice assuring me:
> That by Thy stripes I am healed,
> That Thou wast bruised for my iniquities,
> That Thou hast been made sin for me
> That I might be righteous in Thee,
> That my grievous sins, my manifold sins,
> Are all forgiven,
> Buried in the ocean of Thy concealing blood.
> I am guilty, but pardoned,
> Lost, but saved,
> Wandering, but found,
> Sinning, but cleansed.[5]

MEMORY VERSE

"Yet even now," declares the LORD,
"Return to Me with all your heart,
And with fasting, weeping and mourning;
And rend your heart and not your garments."

JOEL 2:12-13

J OEL
[Judah's Locust Invasion]

DAY FOUR

COMPLETE READ: Jeremiah 20:7-13
QUICK READ: Passages in this day's lesson

RELATED TOPIC NUMBER 1

He is an ethical teacher, a moral reformer, a dangerous disturber of men's minds. He consistently strikes at sins, vices, and lapses and seeks to stir men to holier lives.
— KYLE M. YATES

They were to the people the philosophers, the wisemen, the diviners, the prophets and the teachers of truth and godliness.
— SAINT AUGUSTINE OF HIPPO

It was through the prophets, not the kings, nor the priests that God spoke to the people.
— G. CAMPBELL MORGAN

This last quote introduces a very important comparison: that of the priest and the prophet. Think through the following chart until you grasp the difference between these two very important offices that God used to minister to His people.

Priest	Prophet
Represented *the people to God*	Represented *God to the people*
Perspective: *from earth to heaven*	Perspective: *from heaven to earth*
Position: *inherited,* thus anticipated	Position: *not inherited,* thus unanticipated
Worship leader for the people	*Preacher* to the people
Emphasis on *ritual and ceremony*	Emphasis on *righteousness and conduct*
Character and gifts *not a factor* in obtaining the position	Character and gifts *crucial* in obtaining the position

The false and the genuine prophet will be known by their ways. If a prophet teaches the truth but does not practice what he teaches, he is a false prophet.
—Didache
(The Doctrine of the Twelve Apostles)

REMEMBER
Jesus Christ is
our perfect Priest,
representing us to
God, and our perfect
Prophet, representing
God to us.

If you could read the mind and heart of any preacher who stands up to deliver a message to God's people, you would discover that he is saying one of the following to himself:

- "I have something to say."

- "I have to say something."

- "I have something to say, and I have to say it!"

And once he begins to speak, you can tell which statement motivates him!

There is no doubt what motivated the prophets to speak. The words of Jeremiah could be any of the prophets':

> But if I say, "I will not remember Him
> Or speak anymore in His name,"
> Then in my heart it becomes like a burning fire
> Shut up in my bones;
> And I am weary of holding it in,
> And I cannot endure it. (Jeremiah 20:9)

Today we will look generally at the prophets and try to answer the question: What is a prophet? At least five different titles were given to the prophets. Look up the references in the following chart and fill in the title you find there. Be sure to notice the different emphasis that each gives to the office.

The prophets did not speak on their own accord, but were enlightened by God to see those things which they themselves would not have otherwise been able to understand.

—JOHN CALVIN, sixteenth-century French Protestant reformer and theologian

Reference	Title	Usage	Expanded Meaning
Jeremiah 46:13		300 times	Emphasizes speaking God's Word
Amos 7:12		33 times	Emphasizes receiving God's Word
1 Samuel 9:6		76 times	Emphasizes the prophet's character and calling
Ezekiel 38:17		14 times	Emphasizes the prophet's relationship to God
Haggai 1:13		5 times	Emphasizes the prophet's responsibility

Try to summarize the concepts you have studied today (the comparison of prophet with priest and the quotes describing the prophets) by completing the following as succinctly as you can.

A prophet is . . .

A prophet's responsibility is . . .

What are you learning to appreciate about the prophets that you did not appreciate before we began studying them a number of weeks ago?

MEMORY VERSE

"Yet even now," declares the LORD,
"Return to Me with all your heart,
And with fasting, weeping and mourning;
And rend your heart and not your garments."

JOEL 2:12-13

REVIEW IT!
Our first Related Topic is that a priest speaks to God for the people while a prophet speaks to the people for God.

JOEL
[Judah's Locust Invasion]

AROUND THE
WORLD
The Greek city-states of
Asia Minor, including
Smyrna and Ephesus,
were thriving at the
time of Joel's prophecy.

DAY FIVE

COMPLETE READ: Isaiah 40:12-31
QUICK READ: Passages in this day's lesson

RELATED TOPIC NUMBER 2

There has been a startling realization in recent years that the world seems to be growing smaller. Due to advances in modern technology, we know what it means to be part of a global village and economy. It's true that what happens on the other side of the world can affect us within minutes.

But to God, this world has always been a small global village. To Him, there have never been faraway places. And this is never shown more clearly than in the geographical coverage of the prophets' messages.

Isaiah shares the perspective of God in Isaiah 40:21-25:

> Do you not know? Have you not heard?
> Has it not been declared to you from the
>   beginning?
> Have you not understood from the foundations of
>   the earth?
> It is He who sits above the circle of the earth,
> And its inhabitants are like grasshoppers,
> Who stretches out the heavens like a curtain
> And spreads them out like a tent to dwell in.
> He it is who reduces rulers to nothing,
> Who makes the judges of the earth meaningless.
> Scarcely have they been planted,
> Scarcely have they been sown,
> Scarcely has their stock taken root in the earth,

*Out of the heart of the
Lord Jesus came the
evidences of His love
for all kinds of people
and His refusal to give
up on any of us. I am
grateful for that love
and for that refusal, for
in Him I have hope.*
—KENNETH G. PHIFER,
*A Book of Uncommon
Prayer*

But He merely blows on them, and they wither,
And the storm carries them away like stubble.
"To whom then will you liken Me
That I would be his equal?" says the Holy One.

Over and over the prophets' preaching brings to life the phrases *reduces rulers to nothing* and *He merely blows on them, and they wither.*

In this study, we will compile a list of nations affected by God's message through these very unique men, the prophets. Look up the following references and then to the right, indicate the location affected by that particular prophet's message. Realize that you are looking at only one prophet and one reference related to each location, while in reality there were usually four or five prophets and dozens of references for each location.

DID YOU KNOW?
There are about five thousand languages spoken in the world today. Three hundred million people, representing three thousand languages, do not have a Bible in their own language.

Reference	Location	Reference	Location
Amos 1:13-15		Zephaniah 2:12	
Isaiah 21:13-15		Daniel 8:21; 11:2	
Nahum 3:18-19		Daniel 2; 7; 8	Media*
Isaiah 14:3-11		Jeremiah 48:13-17	
Jeremiah 49:23-27		Joel 3:4-8	
Obadiah 1-6		Daniel 2; 7	Rome*
Ezekiel 29:1-7		Amos 1:9-10	
Jeremiah 49:34-39			

*The location is given because it is difficult to interpret the text.

If you have access to a biblical or ancient atlas, look up each of these locations to get a feel for the incredible scope of God's message through the prophets.

*How you can think so well of us
And be the God You are,
Is darkness to my intellect,
But sunshine to my heart.*

—Frederick Faber, nineteenth-century English Oratorian and devotional writer

Now that you have read a few passages regarding numerous countries, what new insights do you have into the verses from Isaiah 40 quoted earlier in this study?

As you read more and more about the greatness of God over all of history and creation, how does this impact your level of confidence in Him? For further insight, look at Isaiah 40:28-31.

How does it impact your prayer life?

REVIEW IT!
Our second Related Topic shows the geographical breadth of God's influence through the prophets.

MEMORY VERSE

"Yet even now," declares the LORD,
"Return to Me with all your heart,
And with fasting, weeping and mourning;
And rend your heart and not your garments."

JOEL 2:12-13

JOEL
[Judah's Locust Invasion]

REVIEW

1. The theme of Joel is the _____ of the Lord is coming!

2. Our Notable Feature is Joel's description of an actual _____ plague given to encourage the people to think about the end times.

3. Our first Related Topic is that a _____ speaks to God for the people while a prophet speaks to the people for God.

4. Our second Related Topic shows the _____ breadth of God's influence through the prophets.

5. "'Yet even now,' declares the LORD,

'_____ to Me with all your heart,

And with fasting, weeping, and mourning;

And rend your heart and not your garments.'"

JOEL 2:_____-_____

AMOS

[Israel's Plumb Line]

"Take away from Me the noise of your songs;

I will not even listen to the sound of your harps.

"But let justice roll down like waters

And righteousness like an ever-flowing stream."

AMOS 5:23-24

A MOS
[Israel's Plumb Line]

INTRODUCTION

As we said in the introduction to Hosea, Amos is the second of two prophets sent by God to the northern kingdom of Israel. Amos's prophecy is graphic, hard-hitting, and unrelenting. Not only did God's people, Israel, come under his rebuke but also many of the nations surrounding Israel. His message? God is God, God is holy, God will not tolerate sin, God will bring appropriate judgment. And no one will escape these truths.

The book of Amos is colorful and interesting. The prophet's word choice, verbal pictures, and tone captivate the reader. We can only wish that the hearers of his original message had been as captivated — and receptive.

As you study this powerful book, ask God to give you insight into His heart and into areas of sin you are blind to or nonchalant about. Consider the incredible danger of living life in a spiritually haphazard manner and reflect upon the various ways in which God is working to get your attention for your own godliness and for His glory.

Amos

[Israel's Plumb Line]

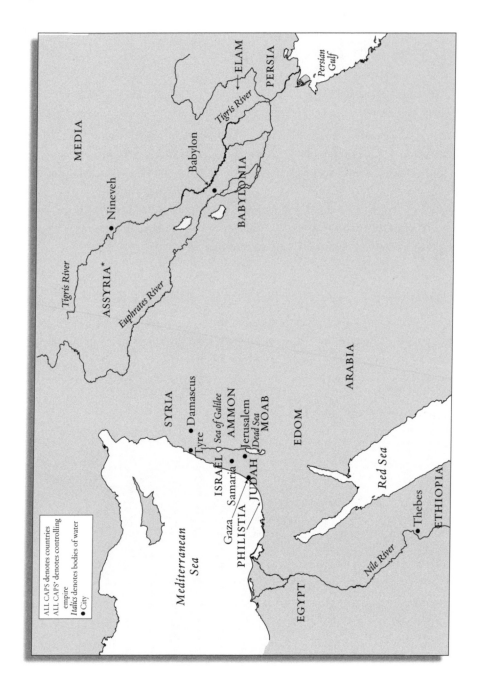

A MOS
[Israel's Plumb Line]

OVERVIEW

WHO: Author: Amos, a country farmer turned city prophet

WHAT: Amos preached the coming judgment of God to Israel and the surrounding nations for their moral, social, and religious wrongs

WHEN: Amos prophesied in the days of Uzziah, king of Judah, and Jeroboam II, king of Israel; he ministered around 760 BC

WHERE: Though Amos hailed from the countryside of Tekoa in Judah, he prophesied in Bethel, the center of idolatry in Israel

WHY: To give the people of Israel another warning that by continuing to cultivate sin, they would continue to accumulate judgment

I. THE PLACEMENT OF AMOS IN HISTORY

 A. The book of Amos is set in a time of _____ for both kingdoms: Israel and Judah.

 B. The southern kingdom of Judah, under the godly King Uzziah, was _____ and fortified.

 C. The northern kingdom of Israel, under the capable but evil King Jeroboam II, was economically and militarily _____ .

 D. During this time, _____ , Babylonia, Syria, and Egypt were relatively weak nations.

II. THE PROPHET AMOS

 A. Amos was a _____ and a tender of the sycamore fruit; he was not trained as a _____ or priest.

 B. Amos was from Tekoa in the southern kingdom of _____ .

 C. Amos delivered God's message to the people of Bethel in the northern kingdom of _____ .

III. THE PRONOUNCEMENTS OF JUDGMENT (AMOS 1–2)

A. Amos gave eight _____ of judgment for the eight Palestinian nations.

B. Amos began with the judgment for the surrounding nations: Syria, Philistia, Phoenicia, Ammon, Moab, and Judah. Then he spiraled in to focus on the judgment of _____ .

C. Amos began each pronouncement with, "For three _____ and for four . . ." to represent the _____ of the people, which had reached its full measure.

D. Amos focused on their _____ crimes and used _____ as the symbol of God's judgment.

IV. THE PROMPTINGS OF JUDGMENT (AMOS 3–6)

A. Amos gave three _____ that each began with, "Hear this word . . ." of judgment, which were _____ .

B. In the first address, Amos declared Israel's past, present, and future _____ .

C. In the second address, Amos warned the people of minor judgments to cause _____ .

D. In the third address, Amos told Israel her fate was sealed and severe judgment was _____ .

V. THE PICTURES OF JUDGMENT (AMOS 7–9:10)

A. Amos saw five _____ that showed the way God will judge Israel's calloused, idolatrous heart.

B. Amos interceded on behalf of Israel, so that the judgment of _____ and of _____ were restrained.

C. Amos explained that the _____ and _____ fruit were Israel's determined and imminent judgment.

D. Amos saw the most awesome vision of _____ standing beside the false altar of Bethel.

VI. THE PROMISES AFTER THE JUDGMENT (AMOS 9:11-15)

A. Amos gave five _____ from God for the people's consolation.

B. God will reinstate the _____ line.

C. God will renew the _____ .

D. God will restore the _____ .

APPLICATION

God's power easily defeats His children's foes. He is our defender, strength, comfort, hope, and security. In Him we take our courage.

AMOS
[Israel's Plumb Line]

LEARNING FOR LIFE

1. Name the five books of the Major Prophets and something you found significant in each.

2. Name the Minor Prophets you have studied so far and the Timeless Principle of each.

3. What did you find most interesting in the book of Amos?

4. What inspired you the most about the man Amos?

5. How did the message of Amos (that judgment is certain) challenge and inspire you? Did this book change your perspective of God? How?

6. Amos predicted that in coming days, King David's fallen tent would be restored. What offspring of David would ultimately reestablish his reign? (See Romans 1:1-4.)

# AMOS
[Israel's Plumb Line]

DAY ONE

FACT
Amos is quoted four times in the New Testament.

COMPLETE READ: Chapters 1–2
QUICK READ: Chapters 1–2

THE BIG PICTURE

Seldom had things been better in the northern kingdom of Israel. Both its economy and its geographical boundaries were expanding. Life was good — or so it seemed. Then a prophet named Amos emerged from the desert and with piercing spiritual vision stared through the brightness of success and excitement to the clouded ugliness beyond. With unfaltering courage and clarity, Amos took the people to task for their arrogance, greed, injustice, and skin-deep religion. His message was that God would tolerate their sin no longer. God had used every possible form of discipline on them to induce repentance, but to no avail.

Amos described five methods of the judgment to come: a locust swarm, a consuming fire, a plumb line, a basket of summer fruit, and an altar with God standing alongside. God warned Israel that He desired their hearts, not their empty rituals. He desired relationship, not appeasement.

A bad man is worse when he pretends to be a saint.
—SIR FRANCIS BACON, English author, courtier, and philosopher

Amos prophesied to the northern kingdom of Israel during the reigns of Jeroboam II of Israel (793–753 BC) and Uzziah of Judah (790–739 BC). His brief ministry most likely took place around 760 BC. As we saw in our study of Amos's contemporary, Hosea, Israel was experiencing a period of brilliance in every area of life but the spiritual. The darkness developing in the religion of the day was masked by prosperity and military power.

DID YOU NOTICE?
Amos's message
contains fewer words of
hope than that of any
other prophet.

Amos means "burden" or "burden bearer." Once you have read his prophecy, you will realize how clearly his name described his ministry: He carried a burden for his people's sin and warned of judgment to come if they refused to repent. The divisions of this burden follow.

Pronouncements of Judgment	Promptings of Judgment	Pictures of Judgment	Promises After Judgment
"Thus says the LORD"	"Hear this word"	"Thus the Lord GOD showed me"	"I will" declares the LORD
8 Nations	5 Sins	5 Scenes	3 "I Will's"
1:1 — 2:16	3:1 — 6:14	7:1 — 9:10	9:11 — 9:15

Amos was from the town of Tekoa, twelve miles south of Jerusalem and six miles south of Bethlehem. Tekoa was located on a high hill with an unobstructed view in all directions. Mountain ranges, wilderness, the Dead Sea, and Bethlehem were all visible.

Amos was a sheepherder (Amos 1:1; 7:14-15) of small and short-legged sheep that produced very valuable wool. He also grew sycamore figs (7:14). His responsibility was to puncture the fruit just before it ripened, allowing the insects inside to escape and the fruit to ripen properly within four days. Amos's work and surroundings color his prophecy. John Paterson writes,

A wicked man is
his own Hell.
—English proverb

> The wide-open spaces in which he lived are reflected in the amplitude of his spiritual vision. . . . All his similes and metaphors reflect the bare, gaunt background of the desert. His task, too, was his teacher. He must be quick to detect the rustle of the gliding snake and know the way of the lion and the bear. Every sound in the desert is significant, and a shepherd must know its meaning. . . . The desert was the school of Amos, and in that school his powers of observation were developed and his faculties sharpened in high degree.[1]

Possessing these faculties and empowered by the Spirit of God, Amos delivered a crystal clear message to the people: Because of their enduring and deepening sin and their refusal to turn to God, their judgment was certain.

We will change our format somewhat this week, studying three Notable Features and then ending the week with our Timeless Principle.

It took a unique man to speak the messages you will read in this book. As you go through the week, keep a log of the clearly expressed traits you see in Amos and also traits that can be assumed from the context of the story. Begin by thinking through the first two chapters and recording your thoughts here.

There's a kind of religious practice without any inward experience which is of no account in the sight of God. It is good for nothing.

—JONATHAN EDWARDS, eighteenth-century Puritan theologian

MEMORY VERSE

"Take away from Me the noise of your songs;
I will not even listen to the sound of your harps.
"But let justice roll down like waters
And righteousness like an ever-flowing stream."

AMOS 5:23-24

REVIEW IT!
The theme of Amos is judgment on Israel is certain.

A MOS
[Israel's Plumb Line]

DAY TWO

COMPLETE READ: Chapters 3–4
QUICK READ: Chapters 1–2

NOTABLE FEATURE NUMBER 1

Before we look at Notable Feature Number 1, read through the following comparison of Hosea and Amos. Remember, both were prophets preaching to the same people at about the same time. Notice how their ministries complemented each other.

Hosea	Amos
Stressed idolatry	Stressed injustice
Commanded the people to know God	Commanded the people to seek God
"I don't delight in your sacrifices"	"I hate your offerings"
Need for the knowledge of God	Need for justice
Rebuked religious iniquities	Rebuked social inequities
Aimed at their worship of God	Aimed at their walk with God
They are a privileged people	They are a privileged people
A national message	A universal message
Complex character	Simple character
Love of God	Righteousness of God
Called for repentance	Aroused the conscience
Stressed image worship	Omitted image worship
Much about the loyal love of God	Little about the loyal love of God
Addressed Israel as a family	Addressed Israel as a state
Dealt with the homeland	Dealt with foreigners
Referred much to the past	Referred little to the past
A poet	A philosopher
A mystic	A moralist
Lovingkindness	Wrath
Sympathetic	Stern

Consider God's wisdom in sending such different men to the same people for the same reason. What might some of the benefits have been in this two-pronged approach?

GEOGRAPHY TIME
The eight judgments start the farthest out from Israel and in counterclockwise fashion close in on the northern kingdom.

Our Notable Feature Number 1 is found in chapters 1 and 2, your Quick Read for today. With the introduction, "Thus says the LORD," Amos pronounced judgment on eight different nations in these chapters. Complete the following chart for the first seven nations. We'll deal with Israel on its own later. Damascus is filled in for you as an example.

THE NATION	THE SIN(S)	THE PUNISHMENT
Damascus (1:3-5)	Cruelty against Gilead	Fire from God and exile for the Gilead people

Systems by which the rich are made richer, and the poor poorer, should find no favor among people professing to "fear God and hate covetousness."

—LUCRETIA MOTT, Quaker minister, antislavery activist, and women's rights leader

Now read God's case against Israel in 2:6-8. Write down the seven sins listed.

In verses 9-13, God reminded the Israelites of His great love for them. What had He done for them before they turned from Him in sin?

In verses 14-16, God made clear the futility of the Israelites in the face of His judgment. What did He say would happen to them?

Remember! If we repent, God's grace is always sufficient to cover our sins.

MEMORY VERSE

"Take away from Me the noise of your songs;
I will not even listen to the sound of your harps.
"But let justice roll down like waters
And righteousness like an ever-flowing stream."

AMOS 5:23-24

REVIEW IT!
Notable Feature Number 1 is God's judgment of the nations for their unique and individual sins.

AMOS
[Israel's Plumb Line]

DAY THREE

COMPLETE READ: Chapters 5–6
QUICK READ: Chapters 3–4

PERSPECTIVE
The first Olympiad
was held in Greece
in 776 BC, just a few
years before the time of
Amos's ministry.

NOTABLE FEATURE NUMBER 2

The story is told of a young priest who, accompanied by his senior priest, spent the day hearing confessions for the first time. At the end of the day, the older priest said to the younger, "You know, I think that when a person finishes with a confession, you should say something like, 'I agree it is terrible what you have done, and I would encourage you to stay away from that kind of behavior from now on.' That would probably be better than saying, 'WOW!'"[2]

"Wow" is what we are tempted to say when we read about the sins of God's people in the book of Amos. In this middle section of the book (3:1–6:14), our Notable Feature Number 2, Amos discussed the people's numerous sins that prompted the coming judgment of God.

As you read the following passages, notice and record statements regarding the people's sins and statements regarding God's judgments to come (see 3:1-15 as an example). Write down as many as you'd like, realizing that some may say the same thing in a different way.

*Oh how horrible our
sins look when they
are committed by
someone else!*

—CHUCK SMITH, pastor
of Calvary Chapel,
Costa Mesa, California

3:1-15	SINS	JUDGMENTS
3:2	*You have a special relationship with Me, yet you sin.*	*I will punish you.*

JUST A THOUGHT
The "cows of Bashan"
in Amos 4:1 were
women of Israel who
lived well on money
taken from the poor.

3:10	They do not know how to do right.	
4:1-5	SINS	JUDGMENTS
5:1-20	SINS	JUDGMENTS
5:21-27	SINS	JUDGMENTS
6:1-14	SINS	JUDGMENTS

If we do not preach about sin and God's judgment on it, we cannot present Christ as Savior from sin and the wrath of God.

—J. I. PACKER,
theologian, professor,
and author

As you look over the specific sins in each of the preceding passages, do you see any broad patterns? Try to capture the essence of the sins in each with a word or phrase (see 6:1-14 as an example).

3:1-15:

4:1-5:

5:1-20:

5:21-27:

6:1-14: sins of false security

Four times in chapter 5, Amos changed the tone of his message significantly from rebuke and judgment to heartfelt pleading. Read verses 4, 6, 14-15, and 24 and summarize in a sentence or two what God and Amos were attempting to convince the people to do.

All the sins addressed by Amos were committed by people of a different historical period and culture than the one we live in. However, sin is sin, and typically, sins of one period or culture have their counterparts in other periods and cultures. What sins do you see in your culture and life that are simply long shadows of the very sins that Amos denounced?

Is there anything you need to repent of right now? Remember, God's grace is always sufficient to cover our sins.

MEMORY VERSE

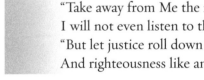

"Take away from Me the noise of your songs;
I will not even listen to the sound of your harps.
"But let justice roll down like waters
And righteousness like an ever-flowing stream."

AMOS 5:23-24

REVIEW IT!
Notable Feature Number 2 is Amos's listing of the people's sins that led to God's judgment.

AMOS
[Israel's Plumb Line]

FYI
A plumb line (Amos
7:7) is a cord with a
weight on one end
used to determine what
is truly vertical.

DAY FOUR

COMPLETE READ: Chapters 7–8
QUICK READ: Chapters 7–8

NOTABLE FEATURE NUMBER 3

Kyle M. Yates, in *Preaching from the Prophets*, writes,

> It would be difficult to exaggerate in discussing the fine literary qualities of Amos's style. . . . One gets the impression that a literary artist has been at work with all his tools and his colors to produce a masterpiece. He uses the metaphor, sarcasm, irony, parallelism, colorful imagery, eloquent phrases, effective contrasts, balanced clauses, and, in many instances, winged poetry of high quality. . . . One sees the orator at his best. . . . There is passion and power in every line.[3]

How little people know who think that holiness is dull. When one meets the real thing . . . it is irresistible.

—C. S. LEWIS, British author of *The Chronicles of Narnia*

Nowhere are these literary qualities more apparent and striking than in the five pictures of judgment in chapters 7–9. If the people had missed the didactic presentation of their sins in the previous messages, the prophet gave them another chance.

The meaning of each of these five visions is graphic, clear, and unmistakable. All are introduced with the phrase, "Thus the Lord GOD showed me." The chart on the next page gives the pictures of judgment and their probable meanings.

Reference	Picture	Probable Meaning
7:1-3	Locust Swarm	A locust swarm wiping out all the crops after the king got what was his
7:4-6	Fire	A fire consuming even underground waters, indicating total devastation by judgment
7:7-9	Plumb Line	A plumb line, indicating the nation's crookedness compared to God's standard
8:1-3	Summer Fruit	A basket of summer fruit becoming overripe and thus useless
9:1-4	Beside the Altar	God standing beside the altar, indicating the source of their sin—spiritual

It is possible to see in each of these pictures various nuances of God's judgments. Describe what you think each one adds to the overall impression of God's warning of judgment to come.

AMAZING! Scientists have determined a total eclipse of the sun occurred in Israel in 763 BC. When Amos began prophesying three years later, this eclipse would have been fresh in the Israelites' memories.

The perfume of holiness travels even against the wind.
—Indian proverb

So far these lessons in Amos have been rather bleak—sin and judgment spelled out in one way, and then another, and then another. But within the writings of each prophet sent to Israel and Judah, there are always rays of hope. In Amos they are sparse—but still there.

Amos 9:11-15 looks ahead to the time following Israel's failure to repent, God's judgment, their repentance, and their long-awaited return to Him in submission. This day was still in the future, but Amos described it in uplifting language in

The Christian must
be consumed by the
conviction of the
infinite beauty of
holiness and the infinite
damnability of sin.
—THOMAS CARLYLE,
nineteenth-century
English author

these verses. Write down the three "I will's" in this passage and explain the contrast between these verses and the rest of the book.

Can you write about a time in your life when you sinned, were disciplined by God, and were then restored by Him? Meditate on the mercy that He showered on you throughout the whole process and then praise Him for the grace that is sufficient to cover all sin and restore you.

REVIEW IT!
Notable Feature
Number 3 is Amos's
graphic portrayal of the
readiness of Israel for
God's judgment.

MEMORY VERSE

"Take away from Me the noise of your songs;
I will not even listen to the sound of your harps.
"But let justice roll down like waters
And righteousness like an ever-flowing stream."

AMOS 5:23-24

AMOS
[Israel's Plumb Line]

DAY FIVE

COMPLETE READ: Chapter 9
QUICK READ: Chapter 4:6-13

APPROPRIATE
Amos's prophecy has
been described as
"molten metal heated
in the furnace of pity."

A TIMELESS PRINCIPLE

A three-hundred-year-old Puritan prayer is preserved for us in Arthur Bennett's *The Valley of Vision:*

> Grant that my proneness to evil, deadness to good, resistance to thy Spirit's motions, may never provoke thee to abandon me. May my heart awake thy pity, not thy wrath, And if the enemy gets an advantage through my corruption, let it be seen that heaven is mightier than hell, that those for me are greater than those against me. Arise to my help in richness of covenant blessings. . . . If my waywardness is visited with a scourge, enable me to receive correction meekly, to bless the reproving hand, to discern the motive of rebuke, to respond promptly, and do the first work. Let all thy fatherly dealings make me a partaker of thy holiness. Grant that in every fall I may sink lower on my knees, and that when I rise it may be to loftier heights of devotion.[4]

Let grace be the beginning, grace the consummation, grace the crown.

—BEDE THE VENERABLE, eighth-century English historian, saint, and scholar

If you only lightly skim the book of Amos, you assume that Israel sinned, God called them back, they refused, and God gave up on them — end of story. If this is true, then the phrase in the prayer above — "Grant that my proneness to evil, deadness to good, resistance to thy Spirit's motions, may never provoke thee to abandon me" — is meaningless.

DID YOU KNOW?
Eighty-six of Amos's
146 verses speak of
judgment.

But there is a paragraph tucked away in these pages of judgment that should encourage the heart of every person sincerely trying to walk with God despite the continual presence of sin in her life. The passage we will study today is straightforward and full of grace and hope. It says God is the God of the second chance and the third and the fourth and . . . This is our Timeless Principle.

Read Amos 4:6-13 and write down the phrase that occurs five times in these eight verses.

Did you find it? "'Yet you have not returned to Me,' declares the LORD." This phrase implies that God did something to get the people's attention, to wake them up, to get them to turn from something else back to Him. What did God do to get their attention and seek their allegiance?

Before God made us He loved us; this love was never diminished nor shall it ever be. In this love He has made all things profitable to us; and in this love our life is everlasting. In our creation we had a beginning, but the love out of which He made us was always within Him. In this love we have our beginning and in all this we shall see God eternally.

—JULIAN OF NORWICH, fourteenth-century religious mystic

The descriptions you have just written are scary: famine, drought, plagues. . . . But the point is not *what* God does to call us back to Him but *that* He does it. He can and will use anything at His disposal, including acts of kindness, to show us that His desire is never to abandon us but to call us and woo us back to Him when we get off track.

But, of course, this is a two-way relationship. Israel, after hundreds of years of refusing to repent, was finally disciplined severely. But even then, God did not abandon them. His goal is restoration. And one day it will happen.

You are not the nation of Israel, but you are one of His children with whom He wants ongoing and unbroken fellowship and intimacy. And because He is committed to that relationship with you, He will not sit back and abandon you when you wander. Spend some time meditating on this amazing truth right now. Then tell God what is on your heart.

Do you know of someone close to you who needs to hear the Timeless Principle that God is the God of the second, the third, the fourth, and every other chance? If you do, ask God to prepare the perfect opportunity to share this truth with him or her. Then look expectantly for the opportunity He will provide.

MEMORY VERSE

"Take away from Me the noise of your songs;
I will not even listen to the sound of your harps.
"But let justice roll down like waters
And righteousness like an ever-flowing stream."

AMOS 5:23-24

REVIEW

1. The theme of Amos is _____ on Israel is certain.

2. Notable Feature Number 1 is God's _____ of the nations for their unique and individual sins.

3. Notable Feature Number 2 is Amos's _____ of the people's sins that led to God's judgment.

4. Notable Feature Number 3 is Amos's graphic portrayal of the _____ of Israel for God's judgment.

5. "'Take away from Me the noise of your songs;
   I will not even listen to the sound of your harps.
   But let _____ roll down like waters
   And righteousness like an ever-flowing stream.'"

AMOS 5:_____-_____

OBADIAH

[Edom's Doom Announced]

"As you have done, it will be done to you.

Your dealings will return on your own head."

OBADIAH 15

FOUR

OBADIAH
[Edom's Doom Announced]

INTRODUCTION

Welcome to your study of Obadiah, a minor prophet who holds a number of distinctions: He is the earliest of the writing prophets, his book is the shortest book in the Old Testament, and he is the only prophet to prophesy exclusively to and against Israel's neighbor Edom.

Because this is the shortest book in the Old Testament, it would be understandable to think that its message is not as powerful or significant as other books that argue longer to make their points. But this isn't true. Compressed into only twenty-one verses, it is one of the most powerful teachings and warnings about pride found anywhere in literature. You will investigate this component of Obadiah's prophecy on Days Three and Four.

Considering that pride is one of the basic building blocks of fallen human nature, you will no doubt find something of value for your battle with it in your study this week. We encourage you to be open to whatever blatant or subtle message the Spirit of God may desire to confront you with as you study and reflect.

OBADIAH
[Edom's Doom Announced]

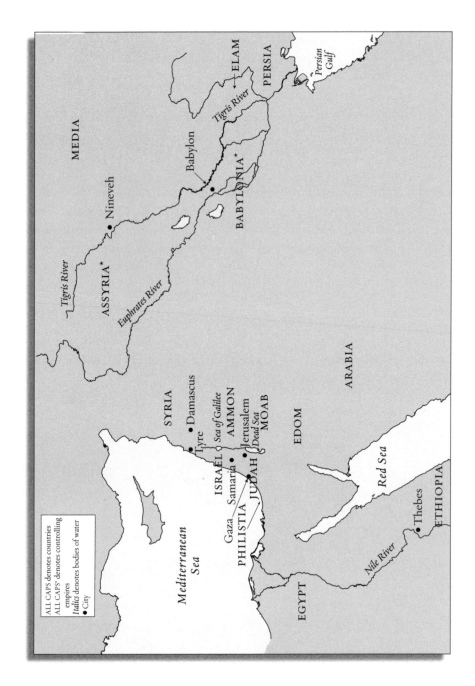

OBADIAH
[Edom's Doom Announced]

OVERVIEW

WHO: Author: Obadiah

WHAT: Prophecy of Edom's coming destruction

WHEN: Unknown, though two dates are possible: 848–841 BC during the invasion of Judah by the Philistines and Arabians, making Obadiah the first writing prophet and a contemporary of Elisha (this is the probable date) or 585 BC after Jerusalem was destroyed by Babylonia under Nebuchadnezzar

WHERE: Edom

WHY: Pride leads to conflict and ends in destruction

I. THE HISTORY OF ISRAEL AND EDOM

    A. Jacob and Esau were brothers who had _____ from the womb.

    B. These two brothers became two nations: _____ and _____ .

    C. Edom refused Israel's passage through their land during the _____ .

    D. The enmity between these brother nations was long lasting (over _____ years) and furious.

II. THE DESTRUCTION OF EDOM: DAY OF DOOM

    A. Pride will _____ our heart: Edom felt secure apart from God.

    B. Pride comes before a _____ .

        1. _____ would bring Edom down.

        2. God would use Edom's _____ to destroy her.

    C. Pride will cause _____ in relationships.

        1. Edom was _____ against her brother.

        2. Edom stood _____ and didn't help her brother.

3. Edom _____ her brother's pain.

4. Edom _____ Judah's wealth.

5. Edom _____ those fleeing or imprisoned survivors.

III. THE DELIVERANCE OF ISRAEL: DAY OF HOPE

A. There would be the Lord's day of _____ . Edom would be destroyed.

B. There would be the Lord's day of _____ . Israel would possess Edom's land.

C. There would be the day the kingdom will be the _____ . Jesus will reign forever and ever.

APPLICATION

Pride causes conflict with God and cruelty among men and comes before a fall!

OBADIAH
[Edom's Doom Announced]

LEARNING FOR LIFE

1. What message do all the prophets have in common? Why do you think this is the case?

2. Obadiah's vision was in regard to Edom. Reconstruct the history of Edom and Israel/Judah (see Genesis 25; 27; Numbers 20).

   a. Who were their forefathers?

   b. What happened in their relationship?

   c. How long did the consequences of those events last?

3. What sin was in Edom's heart, and how was that sin specifically lived out?

4. What is God's promise to Israel in this book?

   a. What does Obadiah say to you?

   b. What are you going to do about it?

OBADIAH
[Edom's Doom Announced]

NOTE
Obadiah is the earliest
of the writing prophets.

DAY ONE

COMPLETE READ: Obadiah
QUICK READ: Obadiah

THE BIG PICTURE

The inhabitants of Edom were descendants of Esau; the citizens of Judah were descendants of Jacob. Jacob and Esau were twin brothers whose relationship had been characterized by enduring strife. We are told they struggled in the womb, feuded over the birthright swap, and lived apart most of their lives. Once Esau moved to Edom, the antagonism between Judah and Edom as countries escalated and continued for centuries.

*In the course of justice,
none of us should
see salvation.*

—WILLIAM SHAKESPEARE,
The Merchant of Venice

Finally in the ninth century BC, God sent the prophet Obadiah to announce the coming destruction and disappearance of the nation of Edom. This shortest book in the Old Testament seals Edom's doom. Because of pride, God's says, "You will be cut off forever. . . . As you have done, it will be done to you . . . so that there will be no survivor of the house of Esau" (Obadiah 10,15,18). After AD 70, Edom was never heard from again.

Verse 1 identifies Obadiah as the author of this prophecy. His name means "worshiper or servant of Jehovah." We know nothing of his family, hometown, or life before or after this prophetic message. Twelve other men in Scripture are named Obadiah, so it has been popular to try to identify one of them as this prophet. However, the evidence is not compelling. George Robinson writes, "For our prophet evidently his work was more important than the worker; and for the sake of the work, the author himself allowed his personality to slip into the background."[1]

The book indicates that Judah, located to the west of Edom on the other side of the Dead Sea, was being attacked by enemies. A number of historical occasions could fit this general description, but the devastating invasion of Judah by the Philistines and the Arabians during the reign of King Jehoram (848–841 BC) seems likely.

Read the account of this in 2 Chronicles 21:16-17 and briefly describe what happened during that invasion.

The message of Obadiah contains two major emphases:

DESTRUCTION of Edom			DELIVERANCE of Israel		
"O how Esau will be ransacked." 6			"The house of Jacob will possess their possessions." 17		
1		14	15		21
CERTAINTY of Edom's Doom		CAUSE of Edom's Doom		CONSEQUENCES of Edom's Doom	
1	9	10	14	15	21

Verses 1-14 clearly indicate events that had already occurred or would shortly occur. Verses 15-21 look forward to that future day of the Lord (see verse 15) when all final judgments and blessings will occur. However, these last verses also point to events that had already taken place (see verse 18).

The theme of Obadiah is very apparent: the doom of Edom. In the next day's study we will discover the many details supporting this theme.

You have been once more warned today, while the door of the ark yet stands open. You have, as it were, once again heard the knocks of the hammer and axe in the building of the ark, to put you in mind that a flood is approaching.
—JONATHAN EDWARDS, eighteenth-century Puritan theologian

Even though we know nothing about Obadiah the man, based on your reading of his message, what clues do you find to his personality and convictions?

In prayer, ask God to give you insight this week, not only into Obadiah's message to Edom, but also into God's message to you.

REVIEW IT!
The theme of Obadiah
is the doom of Edom.

MEMORY VERSE

"As you have done, it will be done to you.
Your dealings will return on your own head."

OBADIAH 15

OBADIAH
[Edom's Doom Announced]

DAY TWO

NOTE
King Solomon of Judah gained great economic benefit from the copper mines in Edom.

COMPLETE READ: Obadiah

QUICK READ: Obadiah

NOTABLE FEATURE NUMBER 1

Because of the length and nature of the prophecy of Obadiah, we will not highlight a Crucial Chapter or a Prominent Player this week. We will study two Notable Features and one Timeless Principle and then conclude with one Related Topic.

In *Explore the Book*, J. Sidlow Baxter writes of the Edomites:

> The Edomite people were like both their father and their country. Their nature was marked by a hard earthiness. They were profane, proud, fierce, cruel; and the tempers found concentrated vent in a strangely persistent, implacable, bitter, gloating spite against Israel, the nation which had descended from the twin-brother of their own national father, Esau.[2]

Love and hate are natural exaggerators.
—Hebrew proverb

It is certainly a Notable Feature that this relationship of conflict that existed between Judah and Edom around 850 BC can be traced all the way back to the birth of their respective national fathers, Jacob and Esau, around 2000 BC. Not only is the conflict apparent on both ends of the time frame but also throughout and even beyond those 1,150 years. We will trace just some of the specific interactions of these two men and their descendants. Where a biblical reference is given, look it up and summarize the event or conflict. Where the information is derived from sources other than the Bible, the event or conflict is summarized for you.

IRONIC
In 586 BC the Edomites helped the Babylonians destroy Jerusalem. In AD 70, they died trying to protect the city of Jerusalem.

REFERENCE	SUMMARY
Genesis 25:27-34	
Genesis 36:6-8	
Numbers 20:14-21	
Joshua 15:1	
1 Samuel 14:47	
2 Samuel 8:14	
2 Kings 8:20-22	
2 Chronicles 20:10-13 (Mount Seir is Edom)	
2 Chronicles 25:11-12 (Seir is Edom)	
2 Chronicles 28:16-17	
587 BC	The Edomites occupied southern Judah and became Idumaea but remained ethnically descendants of Esau.

I imagine that one of the reasons people cling to their hates so stubbornly is because they sense, once the hate is gone, they will be forced to deal with pain.

—JAMES BALDWIN, twentieth-century American author

		THINK ABOUT IT The legendary family feud between the Hatfields and the McCoys pales in comparison to the feud between the Israelites and the Edomites!
164 BC	Jewish leader Judas Maccabeus gained a military victory over Idumaea.	
124 BC	Jewish leader John Hyrcanus occupied Idumaea and compelled the Edomites to adopt Judaism.	
63 BC	Idumaea fell under Roman jurisdiction when Rome took control of Palestine.	
37 BC	The Idumaean Herod the Great became king of Judea. Thus the conflict between Jacob and Esau continued between the Edomite Herod and Jesus Christ, a descendant of Jacob.	
AD 70	The Idumaeans were defeated along with the Jews when Titus the Roman destroyed Jerusalem.	

Obadiah 10,18

What sibling rivalry! What a family feud! Record your thoughts on this 1,150-year path of hatred and bitterness.

Darkness cannot drive out darkness; only light can do that. Hate cannot drive out hate; only love can do that.

—MARTIN LUTHER KING JR.,
U.S. civil rights leader
and clergyman

Read the Christmas story in Matthew 2:1-23. What difference does an awareness of the long-standing rivalry between the ancestors of Herod and Jesus add to your understanding of and feelings about this story?

MEMORY VERSE

"As you have done, it will be done to you.
Your dealings will return on your own head."

OBADIAH 15

OBADIAH
[Edom's Doom Announced]

DAY THREE

COMPLETE READ: Obadiah

QUICK READ: Obadiah

NOTABLE FEATURE NUMBER 2

A seminary professor is quoted as saying, "Brevity is not always the soul of wit, for Obadiah was the briefest of prophets, yet he uttered no sentence which is cherished." Frank E. Gaebelein responds, "Since when has brevity been synonymous with insignificance? Brief messages may sometimes be exceptionally important, as in the case of telegrams or military orders. When vital issues are at stake, words are not wasted."[3]

Obadiah is brief. And no doubt a vital issue is at stake. In this Notable Feature, we will explore Edom's sin of pride and its manifestations and results. This will lay the groundwork for our Timeless Principle in the next study.

Verses 3 and 4 describe the living situation of the Edomites, especially those inhabiting the capital city of Petra, the rose red city named for its beautiful red sandstone. Petra was a place of security and safety. To enter, travelers had to wind through a mile-long gorge with cliffs rising as high as three hundred feet. The ancient city was in an open basin one mile long by three quarters of a mile wide. A fortress was built on the top of a nearly inaccessible mountain at the northern end of the basin. This seeming geographical invincibility fostered a spirit of pride and arrogance (see verse 3). Obadiah indicates that pride enabled other sins to easily take root.

Pride is utter poverty of soul disguised as riches, imaginary light where in fact there is darkness.

—JOHN CLIMACUS, seventh-century Christian monk and author of *The Ladder of Divine Ascent*

The following verses from Obadiah describe the Edomites' sin.
The verses in parentheses are references in other writings that
indicate a similar truth about Edom. Look up these references
and briefly tell what the sin was.

10-11 (Joel 3:19; Ezekiel 25:12)

12 (Ezekiel 35:12,15)

13

14 (Amos 1:11; Ezekiel 35:5-6)

Summarize their sins in a one- or two-sentence statement.

If pride was the Edomites' root sin, how do you think it related
to their other sins?

The following verses describe the judgment that would fall
upon Edom because of their sin. Briefly summarize each
judgment.

2,4

6

7

A proud monk needs no demon. He has turned into one, an enemy to himself.

—John Climacus, seventh-century Christian monk

10

18

Our memory verse states, "As you have done, it will be done to you." As you compare the sins you have described and the judgments you have summarized, how is this verse supported?

What has impressed you most strongly in your study today?

MEMORY VERSE

"As you have done, it will be done to you.
Your dealings will return on your own head."

OBADIAH 15

REVIEW IT!
A Notable Feature of Obadiah is the foundational sin of pride.

OBADIAH
[Edom's Doom Announced]

DAY FOUR

COMPLETE READ: Obadiah
QUICK READ: Obadiah

A TIMELESS PRINCIPLE

Sometimes it is difficult to know:

- Is it self-confidence or pride?

- Is it a healthy self-image or arrogance?

- Is it a true self-appraisal or haughtiness?

Alexis de Tocqueville, a French political historian, approaches the difficulty of recognizing pride from a different vantage point: "The French want no one to be their superior. The English want inferiors. The Frenchman constantly looks above him with anxiety. The Englishman looks beneath him with complacency. On either side it is pride, but understood in a different manner."[4]

One can look down on others and refuse to serve them — and it is pride. Another can serve others but still look down on them as they do so — and it is pride. In pride we can lift ourselves up, and we can also speak disparagingly of ourselves. But one thing is sure: If it is pride, it is not of God.

Write out a definition of pride as you understand it.

Pride is tasteless, colorless and sizeless. Yet it is the hardest thing to swallow.

—AUGUST B. BLACK

Now read the following Scriptures and note what each one adds to your understanding of pride.

1 John 2:16

James 4:13-16

2 Chronicles 32:24-26

Psalm 73:1-6

Mark 7:20-23

2 Corinthians 5:11-13

Deuteronomy 8:11-14

Read Proverbs 11:2; 16:18-19; 18:12; 29:23 and respond to the
questions that follow.
What do these proverbs promise about pride?

What contrast to pride is common to all these proverbs?

THINK ABOUT IT
Pride was key in
mankind's very first sin
(see Genesis 3:5-6).

*They that know God
will be humble; they
that know themselves
cannot be proud.*
—John Flavel,
seventeenth-century
Puritan writer and
theologian

James 4:7-10 and I Peter 5:5-7 contain numerous principles (not formulas!) regarding God's role in helping you put away pride and embrace humility. List as many as you can.

As you meditate on these biblical verses and principles, what is the Spirit of God impressing on your heart? Is there any response you need to make to His promptings of conviction and grace?

According to Christian teachers, the essential vice, the utmost evil, is Pride. Unchastity, anger, greed, drunkenness, and all that, are mere fleabites in comparison: it was through Pride that the devil became the devil. Pride leads to every other vice: it is the complete anti-God state of mind.

—C. S. Lewis, British author and Christian apologist

Memory Verse

"As you have done, it will be done to you.
Your dealings will return on your own head."

Obadiah 15

OBADIAH
[Edom's Doom Announced]

DAY FIVE

 COMPLETE READ: Deuteronomy 18:9-22
QUICK READ: Deuteronomy 18:9-22

THINK ABOUT IT
The prophets of the
Old Testament were
generally unpopular
men.

A RELATED TOPIC

Complete this phrase: In my opinion, a prophet is . . .

A number of years ago the actress Fay Spain, costar of *The Godfather, Part II*, claimed that she had had psychic powers since she was sixteen, with "startling accurate predictions." She has accurately predicted her father-in-law's death, the verdicts of a number of jury trials, and the outcomes of many football games. Her husband said, "She picks winners with uncanny accuracy — I'd say she's right 75 to 80 percent of the time."[5] Not bad! But as you will see, woefully short of the requirements of a true prophet.

The books of The Pentateuch establish the offices of priest, king, and prophet. Your reading for today is the only passage in those books to establish the office of prophet as an institution of Jehovah for His people Israel.

Deuteronomy 18:9-14 describes the *purpose* of the prophetic office. God describes how the Canaanites received revelation, making it clear that this is not what His people are to do. In your own words, what were those Canaanite practices?

Prediction is very difficult, especially about the future.
— NEILS BOHR,
twentieth-century
Danish physicist

REMEMBER
A prophet is nothing less than God's mouthpiece—he had better be right!

Verse 15 lays out the *requirements* for any prophet. What were they?

This verse points ultimately and ideally to Jesus Christ (who fulfills all three requirements) but also relates to any other prophet who was to minister to Israel.

Verses 16-17 state the precedent that had already been set. Read Deuteronomy 5:22-31. On the basis of verse 31 in particular, jot down some preliminary ideas that could form a biblical definition of a prophet.

Deuteronomy 18:18-19 highlights the *prominence* of the prophet. How would you describe that prominence from these two verses?

The prophets did not speak on their own accord, but were enlightened by God, to see those things which they themselves would not have otherwise been able to understand.

—JOHN CALVIN, sixteenth-century French Protestant reformer and theologian

Finally, verses 20-22 relate the *proofs* of a true prophet. Describe how the people were to distinguish between a true and a false prophet. Note: The word *presumptuous* means "to boil up, to seethe." This indicates a blurting out of personal opinion without any backing from Jehovah. Often these "blurtings" would be given because of a desire to please men — telling them what they wanted to hear rather than what they needed to hear.[6]

Combining and distilling all the concepts in Deuteronomy 18:9-22, draft a definition of a prophet that you believe captures the irreducible components as taught here.

Major components:

Basic definition:

The first and most
important thing we
know about God is that
we know nothing about
him except what he
himself makes known.

—EMIL BRUNNER,
Swiss theologian of the
twentieth century

However you worded your definition, it should include these
concepts:

- Chosen by God

- Receives direct revelation from God

- Speaks that revelation to the people

Paul E. Quimby writes, "Prophecy came from a supernatural
source, conveyed through a supernaturally appointed agency,
bearing a supernaturally vital truth or message to the group of
people of supernaturally assigned destiny."[7]

And the apostle Peter wrote, "But know this first of all, that no
prophecy of Scripture is a matter of one's own interpretation,
for no prophecy was ever made by an act of human will, but men
moved by the Holy Spirit spoke from God" (2 Peter 1:20-21).

What will this investigation of the origin of the prophetic
office add to your future study of the prophetical books of the
Old Testament?

Take time to thank God for the faithfulness of His prophets to
speak His word with truth, force, and courage — especially in the
face of incredibly difficult circumstances.

MEMORY VERSE

"As you have done, it will be done to you.
Your dealings will return on your own head."

OBADIAH 15

REVIEW IT!
A Related Topic to
Obadiah is the
accuracy of the
prophets.

OBADIAH
[Edom's Doom Announced]

REVIEW

1. The theme of Obadiah is the doom of _____ .

2. A Notable Feature of Obadiah is the centuries-long _____ between Judah, the descendants of Jacob, and Edom, the descendants of Esau.

3. A Notable Feature of Obadiah is the foundational sin of _____ .

4. A Related Topic to Obadiah is the accuracy of the _____ .

5. "'As you have done, it will be done to you.
   Your _____ will return on your own head.'"

OBADIAH _____

JONAH

[Nineveh's Destruction Delayed]

You are a gracious and compassionate God, slow to anger

and abundant in lovingkindness, and one who relents

concerning calamity.

JONAH 4:2

FIVE

JONAH
[Nineveh's Destruction Delayed]

INTRODUCTION

This week you will study a prophet who is possibly the most famous of all the prophets. His story, at least, is the most well-known. Jonah in the belly of the great fish runs neck and neck with Noah's ark or Daniel in the lions' den as the first Bible story taught to children. But this is not just a fascinating children's story.

Because of the real-life nature of the account and because Jonah's foibles are presented so plainly, its message is as significant and potent as any other in God's Word.

The issues presented in this book are many and varied: response to the call of God in your life; God's pursuit of us for our good; prayer anytime, anywhere, and for any reason; the power of God's message; the patience of God; the grace and compassion of God; the stubbornness of human nature; and many more. There is something to learn here for everyone — especially adults!

JONAH
[Nineveh's Destruction Delayed]

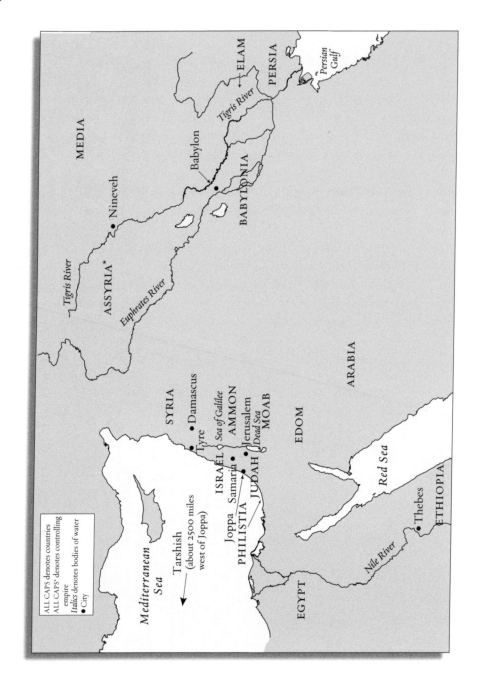

J ONAH
[Nineveh's Destruction Delayed]

OVERVIEW

WHO: Author: Probably Jonah
Main Characters: Jonah, a large fish, some sailors, the Ninevites

WHAT: A message from Jonah to the people of Nineveh, Assyria

WHEN: 793–753 BC

WHERE: Israel, the sea, Nineveh

WHY: God loves and has compassion on the whole world

I. THE DISOBEDIENCE OF JONAH (JONAH 1)

A. God commanded Jonah to go to _____ and cry against its wickedness.

B. Jonah refused and got on a ship to _____ .

C. God sent a storm to _____ Jonah.

D. Jonah was thrown overboard and the storm _____ .

E. A large _____ swallowed Jonah and he stayed in the stomach of the fish three days.

II. THE DISTRESS OF JONAH (JONAH 2)

A. Jonah recognized God is _____ .

B. Jonah recognized God is _____ .

C. Jonah recognized that he _____ .

D. Jonah recognized God's _____ .

E. Jonah recognized that _____ is from the Lord.

III.   THE DECLARATION OF JONAH (JONAH 3)

A. God commanded Jonah to warn Nineveh of coming _____ .

B. Jonah _____ and prophesied to Nineveh.

C. Nineveh _____ and turned from their wicked ways.

D. God _____ concerning calamity.

E. The destruction of Nineveh was _____ .

IV.   THE DISPLEASURE OF JONAH (JONAH 4)

A. Jonah _____ about God's compassion.

B. Jonah _____ life was not worth living.

C. The Lord _____ Jonah from the elements.

D. The Lord _____ the shelter.

E. The Lord _____ Jonah.

APPLICATION

God is a God of second chances. Do you need a second chance? Do you
need to give someone a second chance?

JONAH
[Nineveh's Destruction Delayed]

LEARNING FOR LIFE

1. What was the political climate like in Nineveh at the time of Jonah?

2. What does the book of Jonah tell you about God's view of people from all nations?

   a. How does God's view differ from Jonah's view?

   b. From your view?

3. What are two things that you found particularly interesting about the lesson today?

4. What does this book teach you about the way God deals with His servants?

5. When God asks you to do something, do you respond like Jonah, the seamen, or the people of Nineveh?

6. In the New Testament, Jesus Christ referred to Jonah and to something they would hold in common. What was it? (See Matthew 12:38-41.)

JONAH
[Nineveh's Destruction Delayed]

INTERESTING!
Jonah is the only prophet to whom Jesus Christ likens Himself (see Matthew 12:40).

DAY ONE

COMPLETE READ: Chapters 1–4
QUICK READ: Chapters 1–4

THE BIG PICTURE

German scholar C. H. Cornill writes this about the book of Jonah:

> I have read the Book of Jonah at least a hundred times, and I will publicly avow that I cannot even now take up this marvelous book, nay, nor even speak of it, without the tears rising to my eyes. . . . This apparently trivial book is one of the deepest and grandest that was ever written, and I should like to say to everyone who approaches it, "Take off thy shoes, for the place whereon thou standest is holy ground."[1]

The only difference between saints and sinners is that every saint has a past while every sinner has a future.

—OSCAR WILDE, Irish dramatist, novelist, and poet

That's probably not how most of us see the book of Jonah. Are words such as *marvelous, deepest, grandest,* and *holy ground* overly dramatic? Or does Cornill know something about Jonah that we don't? As you study this unique book, ask God to reveal insights that are truly marvelous, deep, grand, and holy.

Jonah was an eighth-century BC prophet. Second Kings 14:25 says, "He [King Jeroboam II] restored the border of Israel from the entrance of Hamath as far as the Sea of the Arabah, according to the word of the LORD, the God of Israel, which He spoke through His servant Jonah the son of Amittai, the prophet, who was of Gath-hepher."

This historical note from 2 Kings settles a number of facts about Jonah:

REVEALING
Jonah was the only prophet to conceal his message.

- Time: King Jereboam II of Israel reigned from 793 to 753 BC. The story recorded in the book of Jonah most likely took place during these years.

- Family: Jonah was the son of Amittai, named in 2 Kings 14:25 and Jonah 1:1. We know nothing of Amittai.

- Occupation: Jonah was called a prophet. Thus he was a man called by God to be His spokesman.

- Hometown: Jonah was from Gath-hepher, a town located fifteen miles west of the Sea of Galilee and three miles north of Jesus' hometown of Nazareth.

- Name: Jonah means "dove," which probably has no connection with his mission to and message for Nineveh.

Though there is no claim of authorship in the book, conservative scholars believe that Jonah penned this little book himself.

The four chapters of Jonah describe four successive but very different scenes. Become familiar with this chart, and you will be able to think through the story from beginning to end.

DISOBEDIENCE of Jonah 1:3	DISTRESS of Jonah 2:2	DECLARATION of Jonah 3:4	DISPLEASURE of Jonah 4:1
God's PERSISTENCE	God's PROTECTION	God's FORGIVENESS	God's COMPASSION
1	2	3	4

Man may dismiss compassion from his heart, but God will never.

—WILLIAM COWPER, eighteenth-century hymn writer, poet, and translator

The book of Jonah is unique among the prophetical books. All the others focus primarily on the message of the prophet and only secondarily or not at all on the prophet himself. By contrast, Jonah contains only eight words of prophetical message. The book is primarily autobiographical.

Amid the heavy emphasis on the prophet, the message of the book is crystal clear. God wanted Jonah to preach to the wicked

Assyrians in their city of Nineveh to show the world that His compassion is limitless. Thus our theme is God's compassion for Nineveh.

Write down one impression from your study today that is new to you.

Remember our challenge for the week. Ask God to reveal insights that are truly marvelous, deep, grand, and holy.

MEMORY VERSE

You are a gracious and compassionate God, slow to anger and abundant in lovingkindness, and one who relents concerning calamity.

JONAH 4:2

JONAH
[Nineveh's Destruction Delayed]

DAY TWO

COMPLETE READ: Chapters 1–4
QUICK READ: Chapter 1

THINK ABOUT IT
Nineveh was east;
Jonah went west!

A CRUCIAL CHAPTER

The game of chess provides mind-boggling challenges. Strategy, counterstrategy. Move, countermove. But ultimately one player wins. In his book *Reaching for the Invisible God*, Philip Yancey tells the story of how he learned to play chess well in high school but then laid it aside. Many years later he played against a chess master. Whether Yancey made good moves or bad ones, the chess master incorporated them into his own strategy and won. Yancey finishes the story with these words: "His superior skill guaranteed that my purpose inevitably ended up serving his own. . . . When a Grand Master plays a chess amateur, victory is assured no matter how the board may look at any given moment."[2]

Jonah would know just how Yancey felt. Chapter 1 of Jonah, our Crucial Chapter, is like a game of chess. God moves; Jonah countermoves. God responds with His own countermove, and the chess game is underway. Read chapter 1 carefully and write down the various moves by God, by Jonah, and then by God using the captain and his sailors. Describe, or at least notice, the cause and effect relationship between each succeeding move.

*The will of God is
fulfilled in spite of us
. . . and even with us
sometimes.*

*—CARLO CARRETTO,
twentieth-century
Catholic spiritual writer*

Describe your impression of the captain and his sailors based on how they responded when they were caught in the middle of this strategic conflict between God and Jonah.

Retrace your steps through chapter 1. This time, filter what you read and feel through the grid of this question: What does this chapter teach me about the character and the ways of God? Write down those things that are clearly stated about God and also those things that surface as you read between the lines.

Try to set aside what you already know about the rest of the story. On the basis of chapter 1 alone, how do you feel about Jonah?

We have called chapter 1 our Crucial Chapter. Explain the ways in which it is crucial to the rest of the story as it progresses.

Have you experienced something in your life that helps you identify with Jonah's flight from God and God's pursuit of Jonah? If so, describe it here.

MEMORY VERSE

You are a gracious and compassionate God, slow to anger and abundant in lovingkindness, and one who relents concerning calamity.

JONAH 4:2

REVIEW IT!
Chapter 1 is our Crucial Chapter as it sets in motion the rest of the drama.

JONAH
[Nineveh's Destruction Delayed]

INTERESTING!
Just as Jonah was in the fish for three days and three nights, so was Jesus in the tomb for three days and three nights (see Matthew 12:40).

DAY THREE

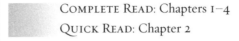

COMPLETE READ: Chapters 1–4
QUICK READ: Chapter 2

A NOTABLE FEATURE

> It is well to keep in mind that we have before us a literary gem and not a fish story.
>
> — J. VERNON MCGEE

Through the years, the fish has occupied center stage. The biblical scholars debate it: Is it truth or myth? Sunday school kids discuss it: What did it feel like to live in a fish for three days? And what did Jonah think after "it vomited Jonah up onto the dry land?" (2:10).

If we keep clamoring for things we want from God, we may find ourselves disappointed. . . . We had thought of God as the dispenser of all good things we would possibly desire; but in a very real sense, God has nothing to give at all except Himself.

—SIMON TUGWELL, author and member of the Dominican Historical Institute in Rome

No doubt the fish sequence is the grabber of the story. But as McGee says, Jonah is more than a fish story — it is a literary gem. Charles Reade agrees: "Jonah is the most beautiful story ever written in so small a compass. It contains forty-eight verses and 1,328 words. There is a growth of character, a distinct plot worked out without haste or crudity. Only a great artist could have hit upon a perfect proportion of dialogue and narrative."[3]

Some of the most beautiful verbal artistry in the book is found in chapter 2. The content of this chapter is our Notable Feature: the prayer of a distressed man of God crying out to his Lord in desperation and faith. Chapter 2 reads like a psalm. In fact, many of its phrases do occur in the Psalms. Look up the following references in the book of Psalms to see the similarity of language and tone: 130:1-2; 18:4-6; 69:1-2,14-15; 116:3-4; 77:11; 31:22.

Scholars debate whether Jonah prayed all of chapter 2:2-9 while in the belly of the fish or whether he prayed some of these words and then later added the rest. But the importance and impact of his prayer does not depend on when it was written. It's clear that this man of faith needed His God.

What do these words indicate that Jonah did or promised to do? (Note: Follow the pronoun *I* through the passage.)

What do these words indicate that God did or could be counted on to do?

In a sentence or two, summarize Jonah's attitude as you understand it.

What to you is the most significant part of this prayer?

Why is it so significant to you?

FACT
History records a number of instances of men being swallowed by large fish and living to tell about it!

Thou my everlasting portion,
More than friend or life to me,
All along my pilgrim journey,
Savior, let me walk with Thee.
—FANNY CROSBY,
Close to Thee

Can you recall a time when you prayed a similar prayer? Describe the circumstances and the resulting effect in your life.

Do you need to pray a similar prayer right now? Use the concepts of Jonah's plea and praise as a guide for your own.

REVIEW IT!
A Notable Feature of
Jonah is his prayer of
desperation and faith
from the belly of the
great fish.

MEMORY VERSE

You are a gracious and compassionate God, slow to anger and abundant in lovingkindness, and one who relents concerning calamity.

JONAH 4:2

JONAH
[Nineveh's Destruction Delayed]

DAY FOUR

COMPLETE READ: Chapters 1–4
QUICK READ: Chapters 1–4

NOTE
Less than 150 years
after Jonah, God
called Nahum to
prophesy judgment and
destruction
on Nineveh.

A PROMINENT PLAYER

On January 1, 1929, the University of California and Georgia Tech faced off in the Rose Bowl. During the first half, Roy Riegels, a California player, recovered a fumble by Georgia Tech but started running the wrong way with the ball. Sixty-five yards later, he was tackled by one of his own teammates just before he scored for the opposing team. As a result of Riegels' error, Georgia Tech scored a safety.

Riegels was devastated. During half time, he huddled in a corner as the rest of the team wondered what their coach would say. After minutes of uncharacteristic silence, Coach Price finally looked at his team and said, "Men, the same team that played the first half will start the second." Riegels looked up and said, "Coach, I can't do it to save my life. I've ruined you, I've ruined the University of California, I've ruined myself. I couldn't face that crowd in the stadium to save my life." Coach Price put his hand on the player's shoulder and said, "Roy, get up and go on back; the game is only half over."[4]

Jonah, too, ran the wrong way. Nineveh was east of where Jonah lived, so he ran west. But God found him hiding in the corner of a ship and in His own divinely miraculous way said, "The game is only half over."

Jonah is our Prominent Player. And his spiritual journey demonstrates the honest dilemmas and challenges we all face in our

We are not at our best perched at the summit; we are climbers, at our best when the way is steep.
—JOHN W. GARDNER, former U.S. Secretary of Health, Education, and Welfare

walk with God. As you read the passages listed below, write
down words and/or phrases that describe how you see Jonah at
that point. Watch for any progression or regression as you go
through the book.

1:1-3

1:4-9

1:10-17

2:1-10

3:1-10

4:1-4

4:5-6

4:7-11

*There are countless
ways in which this
spiritual journey may
happen: sometimes
under conditions which
seem like the very
frustration of progress.
Boundless initiative is
chained to a sick bed;
the lover of beauty is
sent to serve in the
slum; the lover of
stillness is kept on the
run all day; the sudden
demand to leave all
comes to the one who
least expects it, and
through and in all these
apparent frustrations
the life of the spirit
emerges and grows.*

—EVELYN UNDERHILL,
The Spiritual Life

Now, remember who authored this book. Everything you
have read about Jonah, positive *and* negative, Jonah wrote. He
obviously did not feel compelled to put a positive spin on his
attitudes and actions. He wrote it as it was. What does this tell
you about Jonah's response to God's tutoring in the last three
verses of the book?

This small slice from Jonah's life does not portray his spiritual growth as an upwardly moving straight line. And he is not much different from the rest of us. As you look at your life, either in its entirety or just over the last few years, what does your growth look like? Is it a straight line? Are there ups and downs? Do you see plateaus? Describe it in a way that is meaningful to you.

And remember, the game is not over yet. Your God is a God of patience and grace. Praise Him for that right now.

MEMORY VERSE

You are a gracious and compassionate God, slow to anger and abundant in lovingkindness, and one who relents concerning calamity.

JONAH 4:2

JONAH
[Nineveh's Destruction Delayed]

GEOGRAPHY TIME
Nineveh was about six
hundred miles from
Jonah's hometown of
Gath-hepher.

DAY FIVE

COMPLETE READ: Chapters 1–4
QUICK READ: Chapters 3–4

A TIMELESS PRINCIPLE

Jonathan Edwards, the great theologian and preacher of the eighteenth century, once preached a sermon titled "Sinners in the Hands of an Angry God." Chapter 4 of Jonah might be described as that sermon's opposite: "God in the Hands of an Angry Sinner."

Jonah wasn't just annoyed; he was furious. God had done exactly what Jonah knew He would do: show compassion to and forgive the wicked Ninevites. And that, we discover, is why Jonah did not want to go to Nineveh in the first place. If anybody was evil, it was the Assyrians. If anybody was cruel, it was the Assyrians. If anybody deserved God's wrath, it was the Assyrians. If anybody should be ineligible for forgiveness, it was the Assyrians. At least that was Jonah's take.

*Father, You are full of
compassion. I commit
and commend myself
unto You, in whom I
am, and live, and know.*

*—SAINT AUGUSTINE OF
HIPPO, Carthaginian saint
and church father*

Remember, under the leadership of King Jeroboam II, Israel was prospering. Spiritually, they were deteriorating, but politically, militarily, and economically, they were shining. Along with that came a red-hot nationalistic fervor. And because Assyria was an enemy, preaching to them and showing grace and compassion to them made no sense at all — at least not to Jonah. But Jonah was not God. The fact that God was "slow to anger and abundant in lovingkindness" (4:2) was fine with Jonah as long as it applied to Israel. But when God widened the boundaries of His compassion, Jonah found himself in theological territory he had never before traversed. The compassion of God for all people is our Timeless Principle.

Read 4:9-11 and then read the definition of *compassion* below.

COMPASSION (n) 1: feeling for another's suffering or misery 2: pity coupled with an urgent desire to aid or to spare

Putting verses 9-11 and this definition together, describe in your own words what God must have been feeling for the Ninevites.

NOTE
The 120,000 persons described in Jonah 4:11 were either children or adult Assyrians in spiritual ignorance.

What is true of God the Father is also true of God the Son. Look up the following references in the Gospels and based on the definition of *compassion,* write down what Jesus was feeling or describing in each instance.
Matthew 9:35-36

Matthew 14:13-14

To infinite love and boundless compassion I am a debtor. Are you not the same?
—CHARLES SPURGEON, nineteenth-century British preacher

Luke 10:25-37

Describe in detail a time (or times) when you have personally experienced the compassion of God. After meditating on the greatness of that gift to you from God, pray or write out a prayer of thanksgiving.

As people blessed by the compassion of God in our lives, we have the privilege of showing that compassion to others. Paul wrote to the Christians in Colossae: "So, as those who have been chosen of God, holy and beloved, put on a heart of compassion" (Colossians 3:12). Is there someone in your sphere of influence to whom you should show compassion? Ask God to lead and empower you.

Nothing graces the Christian soul so much as mercy.
—SAINT AMBROSE, fourth-century Italian church father

MEMORY VERSE

You are a gracious and compassionate God, slow to anger and abundant in lovingkindness, and one who relents concerning calamity.

JONAH 4:2

JONAH
[Nineveh's Destruction Delayed]

REVIEW

1. The theme of Jonah is God's _____ for Nineveh.

2. Chapter _____ is our Crucial Chapter as it sets in motion the rest of the drama.

3. A Notable Feature of Jonah is his _____ of desperation and faith from the belly of the great fish.

4. _____ is our Prominent Player because his journey with God is so human and realistic.

5. "You are a _____ and compassionate God, slow to anger and abundant in lovingkindness, and one who relents concerning calamity."

JONAH 4:_____

MICAH

*And what does the L*ORD *require of you*

But to do justice, to love kindness,

And to walk humbly with your God?

MICAH 6:8

SIX

MICAH
[Judah and Israel's Indictment]

INTRODUCTION

Since our study of Joel, we have not studied a prophet whose prophetic ministry was to the southern kingdom of Judah. But this week we will meet another: Micah.

Micah was most likely a contemporary of the prophet Isaiah. Though sometimes in the shadow of the great Isaiah, Micah was a powerful communicator himself. At times, a Bible verse or short passage is so clear and dominating that it gives both recognition and reputation for the book in which it is found. This is true of Micah 6:8, which we will study as our Timeless Principle on Day Five:

> He has told you, O man, what is good;
> And what does the LORD require of you
> But to do justice, to love kindness,
> And to walk humbly with your God?

But there is even more here! As you will see in Day Three, Micah had significant literary ability. His insight into the people's waywardness and his clarion call to return to God match the power and impact of any of the prophets.

Welcome to the study of a prophetical book that in the church at large has been too long neglected.

M ICAH
[Judah and Israel's Indictment]

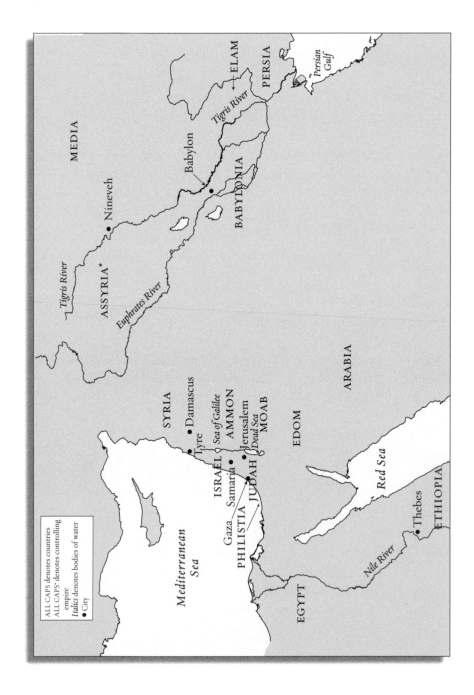

M ICAH
[Judah and Israel's Indictment]

OVERVIEW

WHO: Author: Micah
Main Characters: Micah, the people of Israel and Judah

WHAT: Prophecy of coming judgment on Israel and Judah and promise of the Messiah's first and second coming

WHEN: 735–700 BC (during the reigns of Jotham, Ahaz, and Hezekiah and during the prophecies of Isaiah and Hosea)

WHERE: Jerusalem and Samaria

WHY: The people are warned of inevitable judgment for their sin but are given hope for the future

I. GOD'S MESSAGE TO THE PEOPLE: DESTRUCTION AND DELIVERANCE (MICAH 1–2)

 A. God's word came to Micah, prophet of the _____ people.

 B. Micah described the coming destruction because of their _____ .

 C. The _____ God would send judgment were enumerated.

 D. Micah predicted a still-future _____ for Israel.

II. GOD'S MESSAGE TO THE POWERFUL: HORROR AND HOPE (MICAH 3–5)

 A. Those _____ for Israel's condition were singled out.

 B. Micah gave _____ as he described the coming millennial kingdom.

 C. The Babylonian _____ and deliverance from it were foretold.

 D. Micah announced the promised _____ first coming.

 E. The prophecy of the King's _____ coming was revealed.

III. GOD'S MESSAGE TO THE PROSECUTED: PUNISHMENT AND PARDON (MICAH 6–7)

A. God's _____ against Israel were stated as He reviewed their past.

B. Israel responded to God's indictment by offering _____ .

C. God's second accusation explained what He would do because of what they had _____ .

D. Micah listed Israel's sinful _____ but exclaimed he would wait on the Lord.

E. Micah prophesied Israel's still-future _____ .

APPLICATION

Sin has serious consequences, but the believer is never without hope.

MICAH
[Judah and Israel's Indictment]

LEARNING FOR LIFE

1. What two main messages are contained in Micah's prophecy?

2. What happened during Micah's lifetime that brought judgment?

   a. Do you see any relation to what is going on in our world at this time?

   b. What warning can we take from Micah?

3. What hope was offered to the people who lived during and following Micah's time?

   a. What part of that hope have we experienced?

   b. What is still to come?

4. How does knowing that Christ will come again affect the way we live today?

   a. What should we be doing?

   b. What blessings, listed in Micah 7:18-20 and still in the future for Israel, are we experiencing today?

5. What did Micah have to say about Jesus' birth (Micah 5:2) and His return as ruler over all (Micah 4:1-4)?

MICAH
[Judah and Israel's Indictment]

CONSIDER
Micah prophesied
about four countries:
Israel, Judah, Assyria,
and Babylonia.

DAY ONE

COMPLETE READ: Chapters 1–7
QUICK READ: Chapters 1–2

THE BIG PICTURE

Defendants and jurors, charges and pleas, judges and sentences. Whether it's in a movie, a book, or real life, something about the courtroom world fascinates us. Who is charged? Are they guilty or innocent? And what will be their fate?

The book of Micah depicts just such a scene. Micah 6:2 says, "The LORD has a case against His people," and over and over the charges are catalogued and proclaimed. But in this courtroom, no one is innocent. Common people, princes, prophets, and priests alike are charged with crimes against God and their fellow men. And their sentences are severe: Israel will be conquered by Assyria; Judah will be exiled to Babylonia. But even in the face of a cut-and-dried case and a nonnegotiable sentence, the Judge offers hope. The following chart gives the book's layout.

Justice and power must be brought together, so that whatever is just may be powerful, and whatever is powerful may be just.

—BLAISE PASCAL, French mathematician, physicist, and theologian

"Hear, O peoples" 1:2	"Hear now, heads of Jacob" 3:1	"Hear now what the LORD is saying" 6:1
Judgment on People	Judgment on Princes Prophets Priests	Judgment on People
Hope 2:12-13	Hope 4:1-8,12-13; 5:2-14	Hope 7:7-12,14-20
1 2	3 5	6 7

Micah 1:1 indicates that his prophecies were proclaimed during the reigns of Jotham (739–731 BC), Ahaz (731–715 BC), and

Hezekiah (715–686 BC) — all kings of Judah. This and other facts in the book indicate that Micah most likely prophesied between 735 and 700 BC.

He is called Micah of Moresheth (1:1), distinguishing him from the many other Micahs and Micaiahs in the Bible. The phrase also identifies his hometown as Moresheth-gath, a small town located near the border of Philistia, twenty-five miles southwest of Jerusalem. This fertile area was a productive agricultural belt, which identifies his background as more rural than cosmopolitan.

G. A. Smith says, "While Micah spoke he had wasted lives and bent backs before him — pinched peasant faces peer between all his words." Micah would have understood the phrase from Lincoln's honored Gettysburg address: "Of the people . . . and for the people."[1]

Micah's name means "who is like Jehovah?" This idea implicitly weaves its way through all seven chapters of his prophecy and lays the groundwork for his question at the end of the book: "Who is a God like You, who pardons iniquity?" (7:18).

The courtlike structure of the book, the clear charges of the crime, and the cryptic statement that "the LORD has a case against His people" (6:2) establish the book's theme as God's case against His people.

As you read the book, look for phrases that leap out at you as meaningful, startling, or convicting. Keep a running list of your phrases and at the end of the week review them to see if any broad themes or concepts emerge.

Among the attributes of God, although they are all equal, mercy shines with even more brilliancy than justice.

—MIGUEL DE CERVANTES, sixteenth-century Spanish writer, playwright, and poet

MEMORY VERSE

And what does the LORD require of you
But to do justice, to love kindness,
And to walk humbly with your God?

MICAH 6:8

REVIEW IT!
The theme of Micah is God's case against His people.

MICAH
[Judah and Israel's Indictment]

AMAZING!
Micah prophesied
the birthplace of the
Messiah seven hundred
years before He was
born (Micah 5:2).

DAY TWO

COMPLETE READ: Chapters 1–7

QUICK READ: Passages in this day's lesson

NOTABLE FEATURE NUMBER I

Micah's prophecy contains a unique structural characteristic among the prophetical books: He maintains an almost perfect balance between three concepts:

- Rebuke for the people's sins — all or part of thirty-two verses

- Judgment for the people's sins — all or part of thirty-two verses

- Hope following judgment — all or part of thirty-eight verses

Because these three themes, along with the concept of repentance, make up the major themes of all the prophets' messages, we will spend one day studying each of them in the book of Micah as Notable Feature Numbers 1, 2, and 3. On Day Five we will study a fourth theme as our Timeless Principle.

Whatever games are played with us, we must play no games with ourselves, but deal in our privacy with the last honesty and truth.

—RALPH WALDO EMERSON, nineteenth-century American essayist and poet

All of the prophets — and Micah is certainly no exception — were clear, straightforward, and graphic in their rebuke of the people's sins. Ordinary person, prince, prophet, or priest — it made no difference to whom they were speaking. Sin was sin, and beating around the bush was not an option. J. Kenneth Grider writes,

> They were straight-from-the-shoulder men, those stout and devout hearts who in their times stood up and stood out in solitary grandeur. Chins up, faith up, they minced

no words. If the dancing, drinking society women of Bethel were like "fat cows," that is what they were called (Amos 4:1). Natural men then, as now, preferred a gospel of "sweetness and light," but that is not what they got. These pre-Protestants, like Luther later, took their stand for righteousness against all the rot of their times. Kings and commoners, wise men and empty fellows, the rich and the poor, priests and pagans — they all came under the requirements of these hard-hitting preachers.[2]

DON'T MISS IT!
Don't forget the second half of Micah 5:2 — the baby prophesied is eternal!

The following verses are Micah's rebuke to the people for their sins: 2:1-2,6-9,11; 3:1-5,8-11; 6:1-7,10-12,16; 7:1-6. Before you read them, familiarize yourself with the questions that follow. As you read, jot down your responses in the proper spaces. Whom did Micah address as sinners?

What specific sins did he enumerate?

The people who were honored in the Bible were the false prophets. It was the ones we call the prophets who were jailed and driven into the desert, and so on.

—NOAM CHOMSKY,
American activist
and linguist

What kinds of sins seem to appear most often?

Which of these sins bothered you the most? Why?

Think of the sins in your life and the lives of those around you. Do they differ from those that Micah addressed? If so, how?

After immersing yourself in thoughts about sin, it would be easy to get discouraged and forget the grace of God. As you think about the sin in your life that has surfaced through this study, pour it out before God, seeking His mercy, grace, and forgiveness.

REVIEW IT!
Notable Feature Number 1 is Micah's clarity about the people's sin.

MEMORY VERSE

And what does the LORD require of you
But to do justice, to love kindness,
And to walk humbly with your God?

MICAH 6:8

MICAH
[Judah and Israel's Indictment]

DAY THREE

COMPLETE READ: Chapters 1–7

QUICK READ: Passages in this day's lesson

TALENTED!
The literary device used
in Micah 1:10-15 (see
lesson) reveals that
Micah had poetic gifts.

NOTABLE FEATURE NUMBER 2

The prophet's mind is the seismograph of Providence, vibrating to the first faint tremors that herald the coming earthquake.

— A. B. BRUCE

When a prophet's seismograph detected an earthquake, it always came. Micah predicted Assyria would conquer Israel; fifteen years later that earthquake occurred. He also prophesied that Babylonia would defeat and exile Judah; 140 years later that earthquake rumbled through the land. Not only did prophets like Micah rebuke people for their sin and fervently call them to change their ways, but they also warned them that if they turned a deaf ear to God, sooner or later discipline in the form of judgment would come.

Justice is the foundation
of kingdoms.
—Latin proverb

Before we look at all the verses portraying judgment in the book of Micah, treat yourself to a fascinating observation. *Paronomasia* is a long word meaning simply "pun," or "a play on words." In Micah 1:10-15, there are ten puns. What will happen to each city directly relates to the meaning of its name. Look at the meaning below, read the verse, and then briefly explain the pun.

1:10   Gath — "Town of Telling"

CHECK IT OUT
Jeremiah 26:18-19
describes the great
impact Micah's
preaching had on King
Hezekiah and
his reforms.

1:10	Aphrah — "Town of Dust"
1:11	Shaphir — "Town of Beauty"
1:11	Zaanan — "Town of Marching"
1:11	Beth-ezel — "Town of Neighborliness"
1:12	Maroth — "Town of Bitterness"
1:13	Lachish — "Town of Horses"
1:14	Moresheth-gath — "Town of Possessions"
1:14	Achzib — "Town of Deceit" (literally: "False Spring")
1:15	Mareshah — "Town of Possessions"

*Years of repentance
are necessary in order
to blot out a sin in the
eyes of men, but one
tear of repentance
suffices with God.*

—French proverb

The following verses are Micah's pronouncements of judgment: 1:2-9,16; 2:3-5,10; 3:6-7,12; 4:9-11; 5:1,15; 6:13-16; 7:13. Before you read them, familiarize yourself with the questions that follow. As you read, jot down your responses in the proper spaces. What kinds of judgments are predicted?

What graphic phrases caught your attention (example: "like a woman in childbirth," Micah 4:10)?

What thoughts or feelings are you having right now? Tell God what is on your heart.

MEMORY VERSE

And what does the LORD require of you
But to do justice, to love kindness,
And to walk humbly with your God?

MICAH 6:8

M ICAH
[Judah and Israel's Indictment]

INTERESTING!
Compare Micah 5:2
with Isaiah 7:14. As
contemporaries, Micah
and Isaiah both gave
astounding prophecies
about the birth of Jesus.

DAY FOUR

COMPLETE READ: Chapters 1–7
QUICK READ: Passages in this day's lesson

NOTABLE FEATURE NUMBER 3

In 1828, the English poet Samuel Taylor Coleridge penned these words in a poem titled "Work Without Hope":

> Work without hope draws nectar in a sieve,
> And hope without an object cannot live.[3]

But not just any object will do. Choose an unqualified, unproven, or untrustworthy object, and hope becomes nothing more than "hope so" — a wish with no promise. But choose a qualified, proven, trustworthy object, and hope becomes nothing less than "done" — a certainty with no chance of failure.

The future is as bright as the promises of God.

—ADONIRAM JUDSON,
American Baptist
missionary to Burma

After spending two days studying Micah's pronouncements of rebuke for sin and predictions of judgment because of that sin, we feel the need for words of hope. We can only imagine what his hearers must have felt like. To Micah's credit and for the hearers' encouragement, the prophet scattered snippets of hope early in his message. However, he didn't place major emphasis on it until the latter stages of his preaching.

Remember that the hope extended to God's people was hope following judgment. Even though it was future generations who would see the actualization of that hope, the present generation could take courage in it because they believed they were part of a much bigger picture and that a better day would come.

The following verses are Micah's promises of hope: 2:12-13; 4:1-8,12-13; 5:2-14; 7:7-12,14-20. Before you read them, familiarize yourself with the questions that follow. As you read, jot down your responses in the proper spaces.

Remembering that the reliability of the object of hope determines its degree of certainty, what do you find in these verses that justifies this to be a "done" rather than a "hope so" kind of hope?

List phrases that give the "flavor" of this hope (example: "He delights in unchanging love," 7:18).

Summarize the hope that Micah holds out for the people.

None of us can live without hope. Think back on your most recent time of discouragement, failure, or despair and describe it briefly.

There is no better or more blessed bondage than to be a prisoner of hope.
—ROY Z. KEMP,
author and poet

Almighty God, who always moves with clarity of will and singleness of purpose, help me to live and work with certainty in an uncertain world. Light a lamp before me so that my feet do not stumble. Make my path clear so I may never wander from Your chosen way. I pray in the name of Jesus who comes to make Your way clear before our eyes. Amen.
—RUEBEN JOB and NORMAN SHAWCHUCK, *A Guide to Prayer for All God's People*

Was there hope in the middle of this experience that kept you going? If so, what was that hope based upon?

Is there a situation in your life today that is crying out for hope? Verbalize this to God and plead with Him to revive hope in your heart. Remember, He can be the only sure object for your hope.

REVIEW IT!
Notable Feature Number 3 is Micah's promises of hope in which God is the object of hope.

MEMORY VERSE

And what does the LORD require of you
But to do justice, to love kindness,
And to walk humbly with your God?

MICAH 6:8

M ICAH
[Judah and Israel's Indictment]

DAY FIVE

COMPLETE READ: Chapters 1–7
QUICK READ: Chapters 6–7

A TIMELESS PRINCIPLE

When Jimmy Carter was inaugurated president of the United States in January 1977, he took his oath of office on a Bible opened to what is undoubtedly the most oft-quoted verse of Micah: "He hath shewed thee, O man, what is good; and what doth the LORD require of thee, but to do justly, and to love mercy, and to walk humbly with thy God?" (6:8, KJV).

This verse summarizes so succinctly God's desire for His people and states so clearly what the hearts of Micah's hearers lacked. It serves as a call to repentance, a plea by the prophet for a spiritual turnaround.

Micah 6:8 is the motto inscribed over the alcove of religion in the reading room of the Congressional Library in our nation's capitol. It describes the essence of true religion. When Jesus was asked by the lawyer in Matthew 22 which was the greatest commandment, Jesus answered, "'YOU SHALL LOVE THE LORD YOUR GOD WITH ALL YOUR HEART, AND WITH ALL YOUR SOUL, AND WITH ALL YOUR MIND'" (verse 37). Micah's phrase "to walk humbly with your God" points to that greatest and first commandment. As Jesus continued speaking to the lawyer, He said, "The second is like it, 'YOU SHALL LOVE YOUR NEIGHBOR AS YOURSELF'" (verse 39). Micah's phrases "to do justice" and "to love kindness" aim at that second commandment.

"To do justice" means that we approach every relationship with the principle of equity, doing what is fair, what is right, and

CHECK IT OUT
Jesus denounced the Pharisees as hypocrites for neglecting truths found in Micah 6:8 (see Matthew 23:23).

True peace is not merely the absence of tension; it is the presence of justice.
—MARTIN LUTHER KING JR., U.S. civil rights leader and Baptist clergyman

UNBELIEVABLE!
Micah had to preach
against child sacrifice
(Micah 6:7).

what is honest. "To love kindness" means that we cover all our relationships with mercy, compassion, loyalty, lovingkindness, grace, and warmth. "To walk humbly with your God" means that we engage in a moment-by-moment relationship with God in humility, dependence, trust, and obedience.

For each of these three requirements, name someone you know personally who truly lives it out and describe how you see it manifested in his or her life. Then write down some thoughts on how *you* could grow in that same area.

"To do justice"

Person:

Why you chose him or her:

Personal growth potential:

*Too often we
underestimate the
power of a touch, a
smile, a kind word, a
listening ear, an honest
compliment, or the
smallest act of caring,
all of which have the
potential to turn a
life around.*

—LEO BUSCAGLIA, author
of the twentieth century

"To love kindness"

Person:

Why you chose him or her:

Personal growth potential:

"To walk humbly with your God"

Person:

Why you chose him or her:

Personal growth potential:

End your study by praying whatever is appropriate for you right now.

MEMORY VERSE

And what does the LORD require of you
But to do justice, to love kindness,
And to walk humbly with your God?

MICAH 6:8

MICAH
[Judah and Israel's Indictment]

REVIEW

1. The theme of Micah is God's _____ against His people.

2. Notable Feature Number 1 is Micah's _____ about the people's sin.

3. Notable Feature Number 2 is Micah's graphic predictions of _____ because of unrepentance.

4. Notable Feature Number 3 is Micah's promises of _____ in which God is the object of hope.

5. "And what does the LORD _____ of you
   But to do justice, to love kindness,
   And to walk humbly with your God?"

MICAH 6:_____

Comprehensive Review of
THE EARLY MINOR PROPHETS

Hosea

1. The theme of Hosea is that God desires _____ of Himself above all else.

2. Chapter 4 is a Crucial Chapter because it pictures clearly God's _____ against the Israelites.

3. _____ is a Prominent Player because his personal life embodied his message.

4. A Notable Feature of Hosea is the many ways in which _____ is described and pictured.

5. "'For I delight in _____ rather than sacrifice, And in the knowledge of God rather than burnt offerings.'"

Hosea 6:_____

Joel

1. The theme of Joel is the _____ of the Lord is coming!

2. Our Notable Feature is Joel's description of an actual _____ plague given to encourage the people to think about the end times.

3. Our first Related Topic is that a _____ speaks to God for the people while a prophet speaks to the people for God.

4. Our second Related Topic shows the _____ breadth of God's influence through the prophets.

5. "'Yet even now,' declares the LORD,

'_____ to Me with all your heart,

And with fasting, weeping, and mourning;

And rend your heart and not your garments.'"

JOEL 2:_____-_____

AMOS

1. The theme of Amos is _____ on Israel is certain.

2. Notable Feature Number 1 is God's _____ of the nations for their unique and individual sins.

3. Notable Feature Number 2 is Amos's _____ of the people's sins that led to God's judgment.

4. Notable Feature Number 3 is Amos's graphic portrayal of the _____ of Israel for God's judgment.

5. "'Take away from Me the noise of your songs;

I will not even listen to the sound of your harps.

But let _____ roll down like waters

And righteousness like an ever-flowing stream.'"

AMOS 5:_____-_____

OBADIAH

1. The theme of Obadiah is the doom of _____ .

2. A Notable Feature of Obadiah is the centuries-long _____ between Judah, the descendants of Jacob, and Edom, the descendants of Esau.

3. A Notable Feature of Obadiah is the foundational sin of _____ .

4. A Related Topic to Obadiah is the accuracy of the _____.

5. "'As you have done, it will be done to you.

Your _____ will return on your own head.'"

OBADIAH _____

JONAH

1. The theme of Jonah is God's _____ for Nineveh.

2. Chapter _____ is our Crucial Chapter as it sets in motion the rest of the drama.

3. A Notable Feature of Jonah is his _____ of desperation and faith from the belly of the great fish.

4. _____ is our Prominent Player because his journey with God is so human and realistic.

5. "You are a _____ and compassionate God, slow to anger and abundant in lovingkindness, and one who relents concerning calamity."

JONAH 4:_____

MICAH

1. The theme of Micah is God's _____ against His people.

2. Notable Feature Number 1 is Micah's _____ about the people's sin.

3. Notable Feature Number 2 is Micah's graphic predictions of _____ because of unrepentance.

4. Notable Feature Number 3 is Micah's promises of _____ in which God is the object of hope.

5. "And what does the LORD _____ of you

   But to do justice, to love kindness,

   And to walk humbly with your God?"

MICAH 6:_____

CONGRATULATIONS!

You have just completed set six, The Early Minor Prophets, so give yourself a pat on the back for a job well done! We hope that you have learned for life what the first thirty-three books of the Bible are all about and that you agree with us what an Amazing Collection it is!

So far you have read books by over twenty different authors and have covered a span of several thousand years. These authors have introduced you to numerous historical locations, and you have met many men and women. Some of them were heroes, and some were villains; some changed direction, and some dove deeper into sin. But the One who never changed and remains consistent even today is God.

The Early Minor Prophets did expose to a greater extent the very heart of God. As you begin set seven, The Later Minor Prophets, you will continue to learn even more about God's will for His people. These prophets will take you through the last years of Judah before its people were conquered and exiled by the Babylonian Empire. And you will hear the prophetic voices that continued to speak boldly when the exiles returned to the land.

As you continue, listen to the prophets with an ear for the present. Through these books, God is still speaking to the hearts of His people — encouraging, warning, explaining, and giving hope for a glorious future He has planned for His daughters and sons.

So let's continue the adventure. After one more set, you will have completed the Old Testament!

CHRONOLOGICAL RELATIONSHIP OF THE OLD TESTAMENT BOOKS

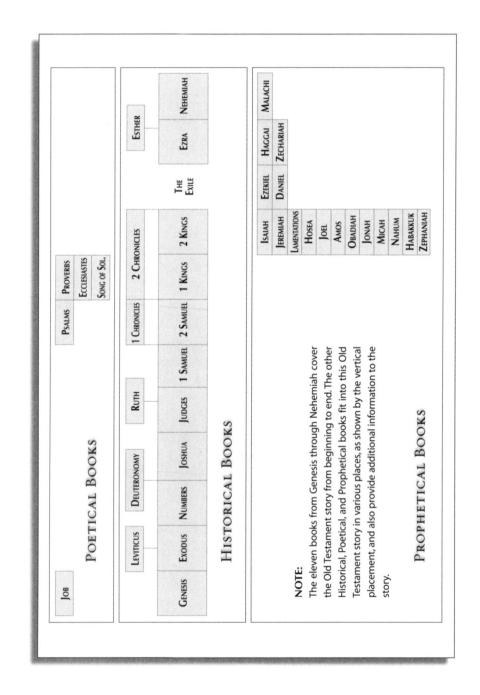

POETICAL BOOKS

JOB | PSALMS | PROVERBS | ECCLESIASTES | SONG OF SOL.

HISTORICAL BOOKS

GENESIS | EXODUS | LEVITICUS | NUMBERS | DEUTERONOMY | JOSHUA | JUDGES | RUTH | 1 SAMUEL | 2 SAMUEL | 1 CHRONICLES | 1 KINGS | 2 CHRONICLES | 2 KINGS | THE EXILE | ESTHER | EZRA | NEHEMIAH

PROPHETICAL BOOKS

ISAIAH | JEREMIAH | LAMENTATIONS | HOSEA | JOEL | AMOS | OBADIAH | JONAH | MICAH | NAHUM | HABAKKUK | ZEPHANIAH | EZEKIEL | DANIEL | HAGGAI | ZECHARIAH | MALACHI

NOTE:

The eleven books from Genesis through Nehemiah cover the Old Testament story from beginning to end. The other Historical, Poetical, and Prophetical books fit into this Old Testament story in various places, as shown by the vertical placement, and also provide additional information to the story.

ANSWER KEY TO OUTLINES

Hosea

I. THE BACKGROUND OF HOSEA

    A. The marriage: God entered into a <u>COVENANT</u> relationship with Israel at Mount Sinai.

        1. God had given the people <u>LIGHT</u> through the law, His promises, and His presence.

        2. God had given the people His <u>LOVE</u> through His provision and His protection.

    B. The adultery: The people wanted to enjoy their <u>SIN</u> and so went "a-whoring."

II. THE MANIFESTATION OF SPIRITUAL ADULTERY DURING THE FINAL YEARS OF ISRAEL

    A. Jeroboam II (793–753 BC) brought <u>PROSPERITY</u> to Israel.

    B. Zechariah (753 BC) reigned six months and was <u>MURDERED</u> by Shallum.

    C. Shallum (752 BC) reigned one month and was <u>MURDERED</u> by Menahem.

    D. Menahem (752–742 BC) reigned ten years.

        1. He ripped open the <u>PREGNANT</u> women of Tipsah.

        2. He died of natural causes.

    E. Pekahiah (742–740 BC) reigned two years and was <u>MURDERED</u> by Pekah.

    F. Pekah (752–732 BC) reigned twenty years and was <u>MURDERED</u> by Hoshea.

    G. Hoshea (732–723 BC) reigned <u>NINE</u> years.

1. Assyria <u>BESIEGED</u> Samaria, the capital of Israel, for the last three years of Hoshea's reign.

2. Israel was <u>DEFEATED</u> by Assyria (722 BC).

3. Assyria <u>SCATTERED</u> the Israelites who survived.

III. THE MARRIAGE OF HOSEA

A. God commanded Hosea to take a wife who was a <u>HARLOT</u>.

B. Three children came from the marriage:

1. Jezreel: God will bring <u>JUDGMENT</u> in the valley of Jezreel, which means "God sows."

2. Lo-ruhamah: "She is not loved" because God would no longer show <u>COMPASSION</u> on Israel.

3. Lo-ammi: "Not my <u>PEOPLE</u>" as the Lord would no longer regard Israel as His people.

C. Gomer became a <u>HARLOT</u>.

D. She ended up in <u>SLAVERY</u>.

E. Hosea <u>REDEEMED</u> his wife and bought her back from slavery.

IV. THE MESSAGE OF HOSEA

A. God deeply <u>LOVES</u> His people.

B. The people had sinned against God.

1. They were <u>UNFAITHFUL</u>.

2. They were <u>THIEVES</u>.

3. They were <u>MURDERERS</u>.

4. Their <u>LEADERS</u> enjoyed the sins of the people.

5. They were <u>DECEPTIVE</u>.

6. They made foreign <u>ALLIANCES</u>.

7. They were UNGRATEFUL.

C. God would bring about judgment.

 1. He would raise up ASSYRIA.

 2. Israel would be DESTROYED.

 3. Survivors would be SCATTERED.

 4. They would no longer have God's PRESENCE.

 5. They would not enjoy the LAND God had given them.

D. God will GATHER His people in the future.

 1. They will once again LIVE IN the land.

 2. He will be their HUSBAND/God.

 3. He will shower them with BLESSINGS.

 4. There will never again be a DIVORCE.

JOEL

I. HISTORIC INVASION: THE DAY OF THE LOCUSTS (JOEL 1)

A. Judah's situation: The people were dealing with devastation from a plague of LOCUSTS.

B. Joel's solution: Judah was to see the plague as a WARNING and PRAY.

II. FUTURE INVASIONS: THE DAY OF THE LORD (JOEL 2–3)

A. The invasion would be like an enormous, powerful ARMY.

B. The call to REPENTANCE (to turn back to God) was repeated.

C. Joel announced that God will RELENT when the people RETURN.

D. THE HOLY SPIRIT will be poured out on all mankind.

E. Joel looked far into the future and described "THE DAY OF THE LORD" and its effect upon Israel and her enemies.

1. <u>ALL</u> who call upon the name of the Lord will be saved.

2. He encouraged Israel with a vision about <u>PROSPERITY</u>.

3. God will have a <u>REMNANT</u> delivered, and they will be saved.

4. Jerusalem will once again be the <u>HOLY</u> city it was meant to be.

5. God will deal with Israel's enemies who will be gathered to the Valley of Jehoshaphat for the battle of <u>ARMAGEDDON</u>.

AMOS

I. THE PLACEMENT OF AMOS IN HISTORY

A. The book of Amos is set in a time of <u>PROSPERITY</u> for both kingdoms: Israel and Judah.

B. The southern kingdom of Judah, under the godly King Uzziah, was <u>SUCCESSFUL</u> and fortified.

C. The northern kingdom of Israel, under the capable but evil King Jeroboam II, was economically and militarily <u>SOUND</u>.

D. During this time, <u>ASSYRIA</u>, Babylonia, Syria, and Egypt were relatively weak nations.

II. THE PROPHET AMOS

A. Amos was a <u>HERDSMAN</u> and a tender of the sycamore fruit; he was not trained as a <u>PROPHET</u> or priest.

B. Amos was from Tekoa in the southern kingdom of <u>JUDAH</u>.

C. Amos delivered God's message to the people of Bethel in the northern kingdom of <u>ISRAEL</u>.

III. THE PRONOUNCEMENTS OF JUDGMENT (AMOS 1–2)

A. Amos gave eight <u>PROPHECIES</u> of judgment for the eight Palestinian nations.

B. Amos began with the judgment for the surrounding nations: Syria, Philistia, Phoenicia, Ammon, Moab, and Judah. Then he spiraled in to focus on the judgment of <u>ISRAEL</u>.

C. Amos began each pronouncement with, "For three TRANSGRESSIONS and for four . . ." to represent the SIN of the people, which had reached its full measure.

D. Amos focused on their SOCIAL crimes and used FIRE as the symbol of God's judgment.

IV. THE PROMPTINGS OF JUDGMENT (AMOS 3–6)

A. Amos gave three SERMONS that each began with, "Hear this word . . ." of judgment, which were DESERVED.

B. In the first address, Amos declared Israel's past, present, and future INIQUITIES.

C. In the second address, Amos warned the people of minor judgments to cause REPENTANCE.

D. In the third address, Amos told Israel her fate was sealed and severe judgment was DECREED.

V. THE PICTURES OF JUDGMENT (AMOS 7–9:10)

A. Amos saw five VISIONS that showed the way God will judge Israel's calloused, idolatrous heart.

B. Amos interceded on behalf of Israel, so that the judgment of LOCUSTS and of FIRE were restrained.

C. Amos explained that the PLUMB LINE and ROTTING fruit were Israel's determined and imminent judgment.

D. Amos saw the most awesome vision of GOD standing beside the false altar of Bethel.

VI. THE PROMISES AFTER THE JUDGMENT (AMOS 9:11-15)

A. Amos gave five PROMISES from God for the people's consolation.

B. God will reinstate the DAVIDIC line.

C. God will renew the LAND.

D. God will restore the PEOPLE.

Obadiah

I. The History of Israel and Edom

   A. Jacob and Esau were brothers who had CONFLICT from the womb.

   B. These two brothers became two nations: ISRAEL and EDOM.

   C. Edom refused Israel's passage through their land during the EXODUS.

   D. The enmity between these brother nations was long lasting (over 1,000 years) and furious.

II. The Destruction of Edom: Day of Doom

   A. Pride will DECEIVE our heart: Edom felt secure apart from God.

   B. Pride comes before a FALL.

      1. GOD would bring Edom down.

      2. God would use Edom's ALLIES to destroy her.

   C. Pride will cause CONFLICT in relationships.

      1. Edom was VIOLENT against her brother.

      2. Edom stood ALOOF and didn't help her brother.

      3. Edom ENJOYED her brother's pain.

      4. Edom LOOTED Judah's wealth.

      5. Edom KILLED those fleeing or imprisoned survivors.

III. The Deliverance of Israel: Day of Hope

   A. There would be the Lord's day of RETRIBUTION. Edom would be destroyed.

   B. There would be the Lord's day of DELIVERANCE. Israel would possess Edom's land.

   C. There would be the day the kingdom will be the LORD'S. Jesus will reign forever and ever.

JONAH

I. THE DISOBEDIENCE OF JONAH (JONAH 1)

A. God commanded Jonah to go to NINEVEH and cry against its wickedness.

B. Jonah refused and got on a ship to TARSHISH.

C. God sent a storm to DISCIPLINE Jonah.

D. Jonah was thrown overboard and the storm CEASED.

E. A large FISH swallowed Jonah and he stayed in the stomach of the fish three days.

II. THE DISTRESS OF JONAH (JONAH 2)

A. Jonah recognized God is ALL-PRESENT.

B. Jonah recognized God is ALL-POWERFUL.

C. Jonah recognized that he NEEDED GOD.

D. Jonah recognized God's COMPASSION.

E. Jonah recognized that SALVATION is from the Lord.

III. THE DECLARATION OF JONAH (JONAH 3)

A. God commanded Jonah to warn Nineveh of coming DESTRUCTION.

B. Jonah OBEYED and prophesied to Nineveh.

C. Nineveh REPENTED and turned from their wicked ways.

D. God RELENTED concerning calamity.

E. The destruction of Nineveh was AVOIDED.

IV. THE DISPLEASURE OF JONAH (JONAH 4)

A. Jonah COMPLAINED about God's compassion.

B. Jonah CONCLUDED life was not worth living.

C. The Lord SHELTERED Jonah from the elements.

D. The Lord REMOVED the shelter.

E. The Lord REPRIMANDED Jonah.

MICAH

I. GOD'S MESSAGE TO THE PEOPLE: DESTRUCTION AND DELIVERANCE (MICAH 1–2)

A. God's word came to Micah, prophet of the COMMON people.

B. Micah described the coming destruction because of their SIN.

C. The REASONS God would send judgment were enumerated.

D. Micah predicted a still-future DELIVERANCE for Israel.

II. GOD'S MESSAGE TO THE POWERFUL: HORROR AND HOPE (MICAH 3–5)

A. Those RESPONSIBLE for Israel's condition were singled out.

B. Micah gave HOPE as he described the coming millennial kingdom.

C. The Babylonian CAPTIVITY and deliverance from it were foretold.

D. Micah announced the promised KING'S first coming.

E. The prophecy of the King's SECOND coming was revealed.

III. GOD'S MESSAGE TO THE PROSECUTED: PUNISHMENT AND PARDON (MICAH 6–7)

A. God's CHARGES against Israel were stated as He reviewed their past.

B. Israel responded to God's indictment by offering SACRIFICES.

C. God's second accusation explained what He would do because of what they had DONE.

D. Micah listed Israel's sinful PRACTICES but exclaimed he would wait on the Lord.

E. Micah prophesied Israel's still-future BLESSINGS.

NOTES

HOSEA

1. A. W. Tozer, *The Pursuit of God* (Harrisburg, Pa.: Christian Publications, Inc., 1948), p. 31.

2. David Allan Hubbard, *With Bands of Love* (Grand Rapids, Mich.: Eerdmans, 1968), pp. 16-17.

3. James S. Hewitt, ed., *Illustrations Unlimited* (Wheaton, Ill.: Tyndale, 1988), p. 459.

4. J. I. Packer, *Knowing God* (Downers Grove, Ill.: InterVarsity, 1973), pp. 14-15.

JOEL

1. Daniel Da Cruz, "Plague Across the Land," *Aramco World*, November-December 1967, 21.

2. Søren Kierkegaard, *Purity of Heart Is to Will One Thing*, trans. Douglas V. Steere (New York: Harper Torchbooks, 1956), p. 44.

3. Albert Camus, *The Fall* (New York: Vintage International, 1991), p. 81.

4. Arthur Bennett, ed., *The Valley of Vision* (Carlisle, Pa.: Banner of Truth Trust, 1975), p. 79.

5. Bennett, p. 83.

AMOS

1. John Paterson quoted in Page H. Kelley, *Amos: Prophet of Social Justice* (Grand Rapids, Mich.: Baker, 1966), p. 15.

2. James S. Hewitt, ed., *Illustrations Unlimited* (Wheaton, Ill.: Tyndale, 1988), p. 455.

3. Kyle M. Yates, *Preaching from the Prophets* (Nashville: Broadman Press, 1942), pp. 42-43.

4. Arthur Bennett, ed., *The Valley of Vision* (Carlisle, Pa.: Banner of Truth Trust, 1975), p. 133.

OBADIAH

1. George L. Robinson, *The Twelve Minor Prophets* (Grand Rapids, Mich.: Baker, 1952), p. 62.

2. J. Sidlow Baxter, *Explore the Book*, vol. 4 (Grand Rapids, Mich.: Zondervan, 1960), pp. 138-139.

3. Frank E. Gaebelein, *Four Minor Prophets* (Chicago: Moody, 1970), p. 11.

4. Alexis de Tocqueville, quoted in A. Norman Jeffares and Martin Gray, eds., *A Dictionary of Quotations* (New York: Barnes & Noble Books, 1997), p. 710.

5. Glenn Lovell, *National Enquirer*, date not known.

6. J. A. Thompson, *Deuteronomy* (Downers Grove, Ill.: InterVarsity, 1975), p. 214.

7. Paul E. Quimby, quoted in *Walk Thru the Prophets,* a seminar of Walk Thru the Bible Ministries (Portland, Oreg.: Walk Thru the Bible Press, Inc., 1977), p. 6.

JONAH

1. C. H. Cornill quoted in Kyle M. Yates, *Preaching from the Prophets* (Nashville: Broadman Press, 1942), pp. 188, 190.

2. Philip Yancey, *Reaching for the Invisible God* (Grand Rapids, Mich.: Zondervan, 2000), pp. 262-263.

3. Charles Reade quoted in Frank E. Gaebelein, *Four Minor Prophets* (Chicago: Moody, 1970), p. 64.

4. Haddon W. Robinson, "Second Chance," *Sermon Illustrations*, http://www.christianglobe.com/Illustrations/a-z/s/second_chance.htm (accessed November 17, 2004).

MICAH

1. G. A. Smith quoted in Kyle M. Yates, *Preaching from the Prophets* (Nashville: Broadman Press, 1942), p. 114.

2. J. Kenneth Grider quoted in *Walk Thru the Prophets,* a seminar of Walk Thru the Bible Ministries (Portland, Oreg.: Walk Thru the Bible Press, Inc., 1977), p. 6.

3. Samuel Taylor Coleridge, quoted in A. Norman Jeffares and Martin Gray, eds., *A Dictionary of Quotations* (New York: Barnes & Noble Books, 1997), p. 174.

LEADER'S GUIDE

1. *Webster's New Collegiate Dictionary* (Springfield, Mass.: G&C Merriam Co. Publishers, 1960), p. 237.

2. John K. Brilhart, *Effective Group Discussion* (Dubuque, Iowa: Wm. C. Brown Company Publishers, 1967), p. 26.

3. *How to Lead Small Group Bible Studies* (Colorado Springs, Colo.: NavPress, 1982), pp. 40-42.

BIOGRAPHIES

Pat Harley
Teacher

Pat committed her life to Jesus Christ at the age of thirty-two after He powerfully intervened and healed her broken marriage. After eight years of study, she began teaching the Bible to women, convinced that it is the Word of God that offers help and hope for women today. She is the founder and president of Big Dream Ministries, Inc. and served for eighteen years as the director of The Women's Fellowship, a former ministry to over five hundred women. She also served as the director of women's ministries at Fellowship Bible Church in Roswell, Georgia. Pat has a master of arts degree in education from Western Michigan University and is currently working on a degree from Dallas Theological Seminary. She and her husband have two married daughters and several grandchildren.

Eleanor Lewis
Teacher

At the age of twenty-six, Eleanor accepted Christ for assurance of heaven. However, when her son was born with a severe birth defect, she turned to God's Word for answers and found not only a Savior but an all-powerful Lord. The Word of God came alive for her, and she began teaching and speaking at Christian women's clubs. For almost thirty years, she has taught Bible studies in churches, homes, and offices. In addition, she speaks at conferences and retreats across the country and internationally. She is president of Insights and Beginnings, Inc., which produced a video series and Bible study to help people understand their temperament types, overcome weaknesses, and use their strengths for the glory of God. Eleanor and her husband live in the Atlanta area and have a married son and one grandchild.

MARGIE RUETHER
Teacher

Though Margie was not raised in a churchgoing home, her parents committed their lives to Christ after Margie was in college. It was her mother's godly example and prayers that brought Margie to the throne of grace. Her growing love for Jesus and His Word led her to Bible Study Fellowship International, an interdenominational Christian organization in which laypeople teach Bible studies. After many years of study, she became a substitute teaching leader and a member of the area team. She served there for a number of years before becoming one of the lead teachers at The Women's Fellowship in Roswell, Georgia. She has also facilitated a Bible teacher-training program for women and speaks at retreats and church conferences. She and her two children live in the Atlanta area.

LINDA SWEENEY
Teacher

Linda accepted Christ as her personal Savior when she was twelve years old. As an adult, she grew to love God's Word more and more. Because of her passion to excite women to know the Word and to see their lives change as they respond in obedience, she began teaching the Bible to women in her community. She has taught Sunday school classes for more than twenty-five years and was a much-loved Bible Study Fellowship teaching leader for eight years. During that time, she not only taught hundreds of women weekly but also trained as many as seventy-five Bible Study Fellowship leaders. She has taught women's retreats throughout the South. She and her husband live in the Atlanta area and have a married daughter, a son, and two grandchildren.

ART VANDER VEEN
Senior Copywriter

Art began his relationship with Christ at age thirteen. In his late twenties after graduating from the University of New Mexico, he began preparing for full-time ministry. He earned a Th.M. degree from Dallas Theological Seminary and has ministered on the staff of Campus Crusade for Christ. He was one of the original team members of Walk Thru the Bible Ministries and served as chaplain for the Atlanta Falcons. In 1979, he was part of a team that founded Fellowship Bible Church in Roswell, Georgia, where he was a pastor for nearly twenty-five years. He now serves as pastor, teacher, and mentor at Little Branch Community Church in the Atlanta area. Art is passionate about helping people understand the Scriptures as the revealed truth from and about God. He and his wife, Jan, have three married children and seven grandchildren.

CARRIE OTT
Editor, Designer

Carrie met Christ at an early age. All her life she has had a passion for words, and as a freelance writer and designer, this passion doubles when it is words — seen, read, and grasped — that attempt to sketch a portrait of the mystery and wonder of God and His Word. Carrie identifies with Mechtild of Magdeburg, who said, "Of the heavenly things God has shown me, I can speak but a little word, no more than a honeybee can carry away on its foot from an overflowing jar." Carrie and her husband have three children and live in the Atlanta area.

To learn more about
Big Dream Ministries, Inc. and
The Amazing Collection,
visit their website at:

www.theamazingcollection.org

LEADER'S GUIDE

INTRODUCTION

Leading a group Bible study can be a challenging but incredibly rewarding experience. This Leader's Guide will provide help with the "challenging" part, as you trust God to produce the "incredibly rewarding" piece.

This guide is not designed to take you step-by-step through the individual studies. Instead, it will offer some general guidance and instruction in principles and techniques. Most of what you learn here will not be specific to *The Amazing Collection* but applicable to many kinds of group study. The one exception is Appendix B.

Each section of this Leader's Guide will deal with a single subject, making it easier for you to return to the guide for future help and reference.

Thank you for accepting the challenge and responsibility of leading your group! We pray God will make this a rewarding and profitable experience for you.

DISCUSSION: THE ESSENTIAL COMPONENT

The words *small-group Bible study* are almost synonymous with the term *discussion*. While there are very significant places and purposes for lecturing (one-way communication), for the most part a small group is not one of them. Therefore, discussion is an essential component of a successful small-group experience.

Discussion is the investigation of a subject or question by two or more people using verbal dialogue. Webster defines it as "consideration of a question in open debate; argument for the sake of arriving at truth or clearing up difficulties." Additionally, the word *discuss* and its synonyms mean "to discourse about so as to reach conclusions or to convince. Discuss also implies a sifting or examining, especially by presenting considerations pro and con."[1]

Small-group Bible studies will not always include debate or argument, but there *should* always be investigation, examination, and the reaching of at least tentative conclusions.

There are many benefits to discussion-style learning compared to lectures or even to inter-action that is dominated by one person. Discussion:

- Keeps every member more involved in the learning process
- Allows for self-disclosure, enabling the participants to get to know each other better
- Helps crystallize the thinking of each group member by creating a venue in which topics can be investigated at deeper levels
- Creates a more informal atmosphere, which encourages a sense of relaxed learning
- Provides the potential of uncovering misconceptions and correcting misinformation
- Fosters more permanent learning and change because people tend to better remember what is said rather than what is thought
- Builds a sense of community as participants cooperate in their search for truth and understanding

While small-group Bible studies that foster healthy discussion will realize the above benefits, the depth of any group experience is greatly enhanced by an able leader. The leader plays an important role in helping each of these seven benefits become reality. For example, in order to keep every member more involved in the learning process, the leader will need to encourage those who tend to hide and manage those who tend to dominate. The other benefits require similar sensitivity by the leader. The remainder of this guide is intended to help the leader maximize these benefits for her small group.

But before we move on, one more issue should be addressed. While the leader is a crucial player in a small group, she should not become the person to whom all other participants address their remarks. One author has suggested that a discussion leader should strive to foster an "all-channel" network, rather than become the "hub" or center of a discussion wheel, as the following diagrams depict.

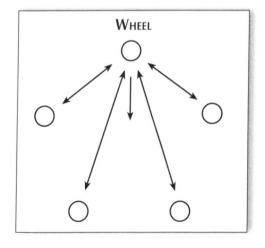

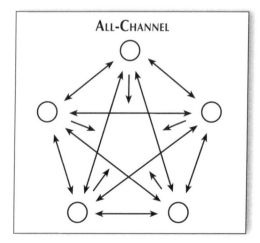

In a "wheel" network, all comments are directed toward one central leader, and he or she alone speaks to the group as a whole or to any one person.

By contrast, an "all-channel" network allows rapid communication without requiring clearance from a central gatekeeper; everyone is free to share thoughts that come to mind while they are still relevant to the topic at hand. Free exchange of questions and responses is thus encouraged.[2]

The leader's responsibility is to continually remind herself of the need for "all-channel" communication.

LISTENING: THE LOST ART

You've probably heard it said that God gave us two ears and one mouth because He wanted us to listen twice as much as we talk. It would be difficult to prove that assumption, but the Bible *does* say:

> But everyone must be quick to hear, slow to speak. (James 1:19)

> He who gives an answer before he hears,
> It is folly and shame to him. (Proverbs 18:13)

Listening may be the most powerful tool of a successful small-group leader, but it is also possibly the most difficult trait to develop. Most people tend to talk more than listen, be more concerned about their interests than the interests of others, and listen impatiently, hoping the other person will finish quickly. True listening is a lost art, which a good small-group leader must recapture.

Listening is not just hearing. As reading is to seeing, listening is to hearing. By both reading and listening, we understand the real meaning of the words our senses "take in."

Consider the following ideas and use them to evaluate your own listening habits and skills. Then, decide which areas you could intentionally improve.

Listening Characteristics:

- It is active, not passive, and therefore sometimes tiring.

- It is other-centered, not self-centered, and therefore sometimes sacrificial.

- It is crucial, not peripheral, and therefore indispensable.

- It is difficult, not easy, and therefore often neglected.

- It is scarce, not common, and therefore greatly desirable.

Listening is not like:

- A chess game — planning your next verbal move while the other person is talking

- A trial — judging what is said or how it is said

- A 100-yard dash — thinking how quickly you can end the discussion

Listening is like:

- A sponge — absorbing as much as possible of what is being said and the feelings behind it

- A pair of binoculars — fixing attention on and bringing into clear focus what is being said

Kinds of Questions:

- Information — "What did you do today?"

- Opinion — "Why do you think that happened?"

- Feeling — "How do you feel about that?"

Kinds of Responses:

- Clarification — "I think what you're saying is . . ." This gets at the meaning of what was said.

- Observation — "I noticed that your voice dropped when . . ." This acknowledges the importance of nonverbal cues.

- Reflection — "You seem quite sad about . . ." This acknowledges the emotional component.

- Inquiry — "Tell me more about . . ." This seeks additional information and often gleans further insight.

While you are listening, consider silently praying for wisdom:

- "God, what are you doing in this person's heart right now?"

- "Father, help me to hear what she is really saying."

- "Eternal Counselor, what kind of response do you want me to make to what this person is saying?"

There will be times as a small-group leader when you will need to limit one member's input to allow for total group input. Your aim is not to encourage never-ending dialogue with one person, but to bring the most and the best out of each participant and the group as a whole, maximizing discussion, insight, and impact more fully than you may have thought possible.

Questions: The Mental Crowbars

Good questions can spell the difference between success and failure in a small-group setting. As you lead discussions of *The Amazing Collection*, the Learning for Life discussion questions at the beginning of each study will give you an excellent starting point. But there will be times when you will want to probe differently or more deeply. At such times, forming good questions will be incredibly important.

Some of these questions may be prepared ahead of time. Others will be developed as you go. Remember, every good question shares some common characteristics:

- Brief — short and uncluttered
- Applicable — relevant to the people's needs
- Simple — easily understood
- Interesting — capable of holding attention
- Conforming — based on the material being studied

As a leader you may ask launching, guiding, and application questions. The following material describes these three types of questions, giving examples of each.

Launching Questions:
- Initiate meaningful discussion on a subject
- May be prepared ahead of time
- Will determine to a large extent the direction your discussion will take
- Are general questions intended to stimulate discussion
- Must be based on the participants' previous study to enable quality contributions
  Examples:
  - "What did you discover in this passage about . . . ?"
  - "What impressed you most about how God . . . ?"
  - "What thoughts do you have about Moses after this study?"
  - "Why do you think God included this passage in the Bible?"
  - "How would you describe the holiness of God?"

Guiding Questions:
- Keep the discussion moving, drawing out the most important ideas and refocusing a wandering discussion
- May be prepared ahead of time as you anticipate the subjects that will be raised by the group

- May be crafted as the discussion is in high gear (This takes practice!)
- Take the participants beyond initial observations and more deeply into the meaning of the material

  Examples:
  - "Sally just mentioned the concept of obedience. How does that fit with what this passage seems to say?"
  - "Who else would like to comment on that?"
  - "We've said a lot of things about grace in our discussion. If you had to boil it down to a sentence, what would you say?"
  - "What we're discussing is interesting, but we've wandered from where we want to go. Can someone take us back to where we veered off the trail?"

Application Questions:
- Are supplied for you in *The Amazing Collection* workbooks
- May be developed based on your own knowledge of the group
- May be difficult to formulate but serve as the bridge from Bible study to daily living—from the head to the heart
- Do not always involve something concrete to do or to change
- Could include meditation, reflection, remembering, or simply waiting on God
- May be questions that will encourage the group to share their answers aloud or may suggest a more private response
- May be specific or general
- Must relate to the truth the group has just studied

  Examples:
  - "Write a prayer pouring out your heart to God in response to what He has been teaching you this week."
  - "Do you know someone who models well what we have just studied? How could you affirm that person this week?"
  - "What do you sense God is asking you to do in response to your study?"
  - "What do you see in this character's life that you would like to imitate? What would that look like? What is the first step?"

Crafting and asking questions are skills that can be developed and honed. After each group meeting, it might be useful to evaluate your questions. Did they lead the group where you sensed God wanted to lead? Which "as you go" guiding questions worked well or not so well? How did the group respond to the questions? Was there any confusion? Finally, make a point to review anything you learned about asking questions each week.

ROLES PEOPLE PLAY: THE ULTIMATE CHALLENGE

If being a small-group Bible study leader involved only facilitating discussion, learning to listen well, and forging meaningful questions, the challenge would be large enough. But add to that the fact that every person in your group will have different needs, temperaments and personalities, approaches to Bible study, reasons for being there, and levels of maturity, and the role of leadership becomes exponentially more challenging.

Professor Howard Hendricks of Dallas Theological Seminary describes in *How to Lead Small Group Bible Studies* some of the roles people play in group situations. You may find these helpful in evaluating your own group's dynamic.

Immature roles

The onlooker	Content to be a silent spectator. Only nods, smiles, and frowns. Other than this, he is a passenger instead of a crew member.
The monopolizer	Brother Chatty. Rambles roughshod over the rest of the conversation with his verbal dexterity. Tenaciously clings to his right to say what he thinks — even without thinking.
The belittler	This is Mr. Gloom. He minimizes the contributions of others. Usually has three good reasons why some opinion is wrong.
The wisecrack	Feels called to a ministry of humor. Mr. Cheerio spends his time as the group playboy. Indifferent to the subject at hand, he is always ready with a clever remark.
The hitchhiker	Never had an original thought in his life. Unwilling to commit himself. Sits on the sidelines until others reach a conclusion, then jumps on the bandwagon.
The pleader	Chronically afflicted with obsessions. Always pleading for some cause or action. Feels led to share this burden frequently. One-track mind.
The sulker	Lives with a resentful mood. The group won't always agree entirely with his views, so he sulks.

Mature roles

The proposer	Initiates ideas and action. Keeps things moving.
The encourager	Brings others into the discussion. Encourages others to contribute. Emphasizes the value of their suggestions and comments. Stimulates others to greater activity by approval and recognition.

The clarifier	Has the ability to step in when confusion, chaos, and conflict occur. He defines the problem concisely. Points out the issues clearly.
The analyzer	Examines the issues closely. Weighs suggestions carefully. Never accepts anything without first thinking it through.
The explorer	Always moving into new and different areas. Probes relentlessly. Never satisfied with the obvious or the traditional viewpoints.
The mediator	Promotes harmony between members — especially those who have trouble agreeing. Seeks to find conclusions acceptable to all.
The synthesizer	Able to put the pieces together from different ideas and viewpoints.[3]

No doubt you will see some of these roles typified by members of your small group. How you deal with members who play out the immature roles and how you encourage and utilize those who take on the mature ones will be an ongoing challenge. Ask the Spirit of God to give you sensitivity, creativity, and ability as you lead. Pray for wisdom to become your constant, ready resource.

Your Leadership: A Spiritual Endeavor

Before we move on, it is important to remember that beyond understanding and fostering discussion, learning to listen well, developing your skill in fashioning questions, and learning to lead different kinds of people, it is God who supplies the grace and strength that will carry you through the challenges of leadership.

This Leader's Guide has focused so far on you and your best efforts, but in truth you will accomplish absolutely nothing of eternal value unless the Spirit of God takes your faithful efforts and infuses them with His enabling power and grace.

For this reason, we encourage you to prepare and lead in complete humility, dependence, and trust, remembering these critical precepts:

I can do all things through Him who strengthens me. (Philippians 4:13)

"My grace is sufficient for you, for power is perfected in weakness." (2 Corinthians 12:9)

"I am the vine, you are the branches; he who abides in Me and I in him, he bears much fruit, for apart from Me you can do nothing." (John 15:5)

Finally, be strong in the Lord and in the strength of His might. Put on the full armor of God, so that you will be able to stand firm against the schemes of the devil. (Ephesians 6:10-11)

Our prayer for you is that of Paul's prayers for the Ephesians:

> That the God of our Lord Jesus Christ, the Father of glory, may give to you a spirit of wisdom and of revelation in the knowledge of Him. I pray that the eyes of your heart may be enlightened, so that you will know what is the hope of His calling, what are the riches of the glory of His inheritance in the saints, and what is the surpassing greatness of His power toward us who believe. These are in accordance with the working of the strength of His might. . . . [And] that He would grant you, according to the riches of His glory, to be strengthened with power through His Spirit in the inner man, so that Christ may dwell in your hearts through faith; and that you, being rooted and grounded in love, may be able to comprehend with all the saints what is the breadth and length and height and depth, and to know the love of Christ which surpasses knowledge, that you may be filled up to all the fullness of God. Now to Him who is able to do far more abundantly beyond all that we ask or think, according to the power that works within us, to Him be the glory in the church and in Christ Jesus to all generations forever and ever. Amen. (Ephesians 1:17-19; 3:16-21)

APPENDIX A

THE EFFECTIVE DISCUSSION LEADER: A WORTHY GOAL

This section presents a model for the effective discussion leader (EDL). You may not demonstrate every characteristic listed, nor do you need to. Some of these things you will do very well; others you will do okay; still others may be a weak area for you. That is just fine. Consider this list simply an ideal to aim for. Our hope is that it will motivate you to grow as a small-group leader by revealing your areas of strength and highlighting your areas of weakness for which you may need help. God never said He could use only perfect people in ministry. In fact, your limitations in one or more of these areas may allow for others in the group to come alongside and complement you by contributing their strengths.

You may choose to use this list with a group of leaders to discuss your common ministries and responsibilities and share with each other challenges and successes you've experienced as leaders. Hearing others' thoughts about each of these characteristics might encourage you as you continue to grow.

What key characteristics make an effective discussion leader?

1. EDLs have a good grasp of the material to be discussed.
   - They have studied the material in advance.
   - They have a clear purpose for the meeting.
   - They have an introduction planned.
   - They have questions planned.
   - They have a tentative conclusion in mind.
   - They have examined their own life in relation to the truth of the study.
   - They seek to be diligent workers who accurately handle the word of truth (see 2 Timothy 2:15).

2. EDLs are skilled in organizing group thinking.
   - They know how to use questions.

- They can detect tangents and gently but firmly bring the discussion back on track.

3. EDLs are open-minded.
   - They express judgments in a conditional way.
   - They encourage consideration of all points of view.
   - They encourage open-mindedness on the part of all the members.
   - They are able to handle incorrect answers by inviting further questioning or discussion.

4. EDLs are active participants.
   - They talk frequently yet not excessively.
   - They are not defensive or sensitive to disagreement or criticism.

5. EDLs are facilitators.
   - They do not give dictatorial directions.
   - They encourage participation by all.
   - They encourage interaction among all members.
   - They are able to manage members who tend to dominate discussion.
   - They are able to stimulate and involve shy or reticent members in nonthreatening ways.

6. EDLs speak well.
   - They speak clearly.
   - They speak in a concise, pertinent way.
   - They are not tactless, chattering, offensive speakers.

7. EDLs have respect for and sensitivity to others.
   - They are empathetic.
   - They do not attack others.
   - They do not cause others to "lose face."
   - They are aware of how others are reacting.
   - They are patient.

8. EDLs are self-controlled.
   - They can remain impartial when necessary.

- They can express their feelings in a direct, yet nonaccusatory manner.

9. EDLs can assume different roles.

   - They can give encouragement.
   - They can give direction when necessary.
   - They can insert humor to break the tension when appropriate.
   - They can lead the group in prayer to seek wisdom.
   - They can give personal attention to needy members.

10. EDLs give credit to the group and its members.

    - They praise the group for insights and progress.
    - They stress teamwork.
    - They make all the members feel important.
    - They value others as their equals.
    - They "do nothing from selfishness or empty conceit" but regard others as more important than themselves (Philippians 2:3).

11. EDLs are authentically transparent.

    - They share personal illustrations.
    - They share personal weaknesses, frustrations, pressures, and failures without seeking undue personal attention.
    - They share personal feelings.
    - They share personal requests.
    - They plan ahead so all this can be done with taste and genuineness.

12. EDLs are enthusiastic.

    - They pour themselves into the subject and the discussion of it.
    - They allow the subject to be poured into them by God prior to the discussion.
    - They recognize that genuine enthusiasm is a powerful motivator for others.

13. EDLs are properly critical and evaluative of their leadership.

    - They constantly look for ways to improve.
    - They regularly seek feedback and advice.
    - They consistently evaluate the various aspects of their leadership role.

- They remember that evaluation is not comparing themselves with others but is seeking the Holy Spirit's input on possible improvement.

14. EDLs know that leadership is a spiritual endeavor.

- They regularly admit to God that apart from Him they can do nothing (see John 15:5).

- They confidently say "I can do all things" and then humbly add "through Him who strengthens me" (Philippians 4:13).

- They never forget God's promise that "My grace is sufficient for you" (2 Corinthians 12:9).

APPENDIX B

SUGGESTED FORMATS FOR *THE AMAZING COLLECTION*

The Amazing Collection is intentionally flexible to accommodate a variety of teaching settings and calendars. It is possible to complete the study of all sixty-six books of the Bible in two years by teaching a book a week for thirty-three weeks each year (excluding summers and holidays).

Another option would be to go through the material in three years, teaching a book a week for twenty-two weeks each year, perhaps beginning in September and going through April. Also, for individuals, the program could be completed in approximately fifteen months, studying a book a week for sixty-six consecutive weeks.

There is flexibility in each individual session as well. Sessions might last an hour, in which the group watches the video (forty-five minutes) and allows fifteen minutes for discussion. Or, a 1.5-hour format could include the video, fifteen minutes for refreshments, fifteen for discussion, and fifteen for homework review. If time permits, two-hour sessions could include the video, refreshments, thirty minutes for discussion, and thirty for homework review.

Maybe you'll discover another format that suits your group to a tee. Feel free to use it!

APPENDIX C

SHARING THE GOSPEL

Leaders should be sensitive to the fact that some group members may have an interest in the Bible without having established a personal relationship with its central figure, Jesus Christ.

Sharing the gospel is quite easy for some people and more challenging for others. But if you sense that there are members in your group who would benefit from a clear explanation of salvation, by all means, offer one! There may even be "natural" openings during your course of study (at the end of a book or workbook or during your study of the Gospels or the book of Romans) when the gospel seems to "tell itself." In addition, the vast majority of discussion questions (Old and New Testament) contain a question that points directly to the person of Jesus Christ. These are "teachable moments." Don't miss them.

Several excellent tools exist that can help you walk an unbeliever through the basics of salvation. *The Four Spiritual Laws, Steps to Peace with God, My Heart — Christ's Home,* and *The Roman Road* are just a few. The leaders in your church may be able to provide you with one or more of them.

Although there are many excellent video testimonies throughout *The Amazing Collection*, it may be appropriate at some point to briefly share your own personal testimony with your group or with one or more of its members. It may help to think of your "story" in four parts: your life before Christ, how you came to know and understand your need for forgiveness and reconciliation with God, what Christ did on your behalf on the cross, and how your life is different today having accepted His atoning sacrifice on your behalf. This is your story! Pray for a sensitive heart, the right timing, and the right words to share it when the Holy Spirit leads you to do so.

It is our prayer that no one would complete *The Amazing Collection* without a personal, saving knowledge of our Savior, the Lord Jesus Christ.